A STYLE MANUAL
FOR TECHNICAL WRITERS
AND EDITORS

A STYLE MANUAL
FOR TECHNICAL WRITERS
AND EDITORS

Edited by

S. J. REISMAN
Manager
Research Technical Publications
Lockheed Missiles and Space Company
Sunnyvale, California

The Macmillan Company
New York

SECOND PRINTING, 1962

Library of Congress catalog card number: 62-8748

The Macmillan Company, New York
Brett-Macmillan Ltd., Galt, Ontario

Printed in the United States of America

PREFACE

One of the chief products of industrial firms and governmental agencies is technical writing—information in the form of reports or technical manuals.

The technical manual or the report of research undertaken is but one end of the broad span of technical writing for which a scientist or engineer is responsible. At the opposite end of the span is a proposal, and at intermediate points are journal articles, various memoranda, and interdepartmental communications.

A research-project report records exactly what was learned from a particular effort. A technical manual explains how to install, operate, and maintain complex equipment. Journal articles tell the writer's contemporaries of his work, while memoranda and interdepartmental communications present details of his work to superiors or to associates. A successful proposal shows a prospective customer why and how certain research or manufacturing should be undertaken and convinces him of the company's ability to undertake it. It tells what results may be expected, how much the project will cost, and how it is to be conducted. Thus, the ability of a scientist or an engineer to write well plays a key part in his work. It starts his project and marks its end. It helps to establish his standing among his peers and provides an effective way of informing his coworkers of the problems he is attempting to solve and of his success in solving them.

Good technical writing is necessary if a publication is to be useful. Companies expect their scientists and engineers to report the results of their investigations clearly and concisely. However good the research and development program may have been, unless the report succeeds in presenting the results clearly and concisely, much irreplaceable time and effort will have been lost. If a poor technical manual is produced, the equipment may become inoperable in the field.

Good technical writing is most often characterized by an uncomplicated, direct style and by careful diction. Consider, for example, such science classics as Faraday's Researches in Electricity, Millikan's The Electron, and Bragg's The World of Sound. The writing in these books is clear, concise, and well organized; the language never interferes with the ideas. Such clarity did not just happen. The authors worked hard to communicate their ideas, for writing well is never easy. It is both difficult and time-consuming; and not many authors have sufficient time or energy to write and rewrite, to think and rethink, to edit and reedit their writing so that it is clear and unambiguous.

Most companies recognize the need for clear, well-organized, timely publications. As a result, they have technical publications departments with personnel available to assist and even to collaborate in the various writing tasks with which busy scientists and engineers may be burdened. How the technical publications department works is discussed in Part One of this Guide.

Part Two deals with the special features of the technical report, the technical proposal, and the technical manual. Format considerations common to these three types of publications are treated in Part Three. Attention is given to such items as headings and pagination, tables, illustrations, equations, and references. Although matters of format are considered further in Part Four, emphasis is placed on the individual items of a publication, and on the specific aspects of style and accepted usage in sentence structure and paragraphing, punctuation, spelling and compounding, numbers, and abbreviations.

Appendix A provides sample pages of the various aspects discussed in the main text. Appendix B presents an annotated list of references for those interested in obtaining further information on style, grammar, and technical writing. Finally, Appendix C contains the marks commonly used for editing and proofreading typed copy.

Today most technical reports and proposals, certain classes of manuals, and much technical promotional material are produced from typewritten copy and printed on small offset presses — the so-called cold-type processes. This Guide is published as an example of the kind of publication that can be produced by such processes. Most of the recommended practices and procedures, however, are equally applicable to hot-type.

Exhaustive treatment is not intended in this Guide. However, enough material is presented to provide an objective basis for evaluating a manuscript and hence for increasing the likelihood that an effective publication will be provided. The Guide can also be used to help achieve uniformity and standardization of publication practices.

ACKNOWLEDGMENTS

The editor gratefully acknowledges major contributions from the following persons:

> Kenneth A. Anderson
>
> Margarett N. Collins
>
> Leon H. Goldich
>
> Harold S. Leefeldt
>
> Emlen T. Littell
>
> Richard A. Schweinsberger
>
> Homer E. Shaw
>
> Jarvis Todd
>
> Graham Unikel
>
> Virginia P. Whipple

Reproduction copy was typed by the Technical Typing Group of Research Technical Publications, Lockheed Missiles and Space Company. The painstaking work of this group is warmly appreciated.

CONTENTS

ILLUSTRATIONS

PART 1

THE TECHNICAL PUBLICATIONS DEPARTMENT

Chapter 1
PERSONNEL AND FUNCTIONS

TECHNICAL PUBLICATIONS

Manager

Reproduction

Art

Typing

Editorial

1.1 Departmental Organization

Since the beginning of World War II, a field of specialization which has grown tremendously is publications engineering. In industry, this field is largely the concern of technical publications departments that normally provide writing and editorial services, as well as art, typing, photography, and reproduction services.

Most technical publications departments consist of at least four groups:

- Editorial
- Art
- Technical Typing
- Reproduction

1.2 Editorial Group

The editorial group consists of publications engineers — technical writers and editors. The publications engineer is a specialist in scientific and engineering communication. He is responsible for writing technical manuals, training manuals, and special brochures, as well as for editing reports, proposals, scientific papers, and other communications written by scientists and engineers. At times he must help to prepare presentations, such as management or sales reports, exhibits, and slides. Almost always he works against a difficult deadline with little or no control over his sources of information.

The difference between a technical writer and a technical editor is in the kind of work each does. A technical writer prepares manuscript based on information supplied by scientists or engineers. An editor, on the other hand, works with manuscript prepared by research personnel. A technical writer on one assignment may work as an editor on the next, or he may work in both capacities on a single assignment.

A publications engineer must have a general background in science or engineering, writing skill, and the ability to edit technical writing. He must also have a thorough understanding of the typing, artwork, photography, and reproduction activities. To ensure the timely completion of a publication, he must be able to schedule and direct these activities. To work effectively, he must be able to gain the respect and co-operation of scientists, engineers, vendors, and suppliers of services. In addition, he must be familiar with government handbook specifications; with research, engineering, and manufacturing procedures; and with recent state-of-the-art advances in the equipment, organization, and methods of his profession.

Within a few hours, most qualified writers and editors can feel at home with any technical manuscript.

Although their technical education is usually less specialized than that of research scientists and engineers, many have a Bachelor's or Master's degree in engineering or a physical science, and a few have Ph.D.'s. Usually they have had considerable training or experience in language, literature, and writing.

The personnel of the technical publications department know the importance of technical publications and are constantly seeking to improve the quality of publications identified with the company or agency for which they work. Technical personnel, therefore, should not hesitate to confer with the writers and editors on any problem concerning publications.

1.3 Art Group

The art group consists of technical artists who have had varying amounts of professional education. Many are college graduates or have attended vocational art schools. Many have done artwork on a free-lance basis and in the aircraft and electronics industries. Their experience includes advertising, display, and product-design activities.

As a result of their education and experience, the technical artists are able to produce almost any kind of artwork required, from orthographic, isometric, and perspective projections to freehand drawings, paintings, and airbrush presentations. They are skilled in the use of Zip-a-Tone and other shading tints to produce simulated halftone illustrations. (See Chapter 8.)

1.4 Technical Typing Group

The technical typing group consists of specially trained personnel who are responsible for typing reproduction copy on paper plates, or on bond, vellum, or Ditto masters. They are able to operate electric typewriters with standard, gothic, and mathematical typefaces; proportional-spacing typewriters with several typefaces; and other special typing machines that offer a variety of type styles.

Technical typists have a thorough understanding of format, layout, and procedures for correcting all types of reproducible material.

1.5 Reproduction Group

The reproduction group usually consists of both printers and photographers. The printers operate the small offset presses normally used to reproduce the relatively small number of copies required for most technical publications. In addition, the group is responsible for collating and binding. In most printshops, the printers make the Xerox plates (page 2-8), and the photographers make the metal or metal-like offset plates for material, including halftones, that cannot be reproduced well by means of a Xerox plate. The reproduction group usually includes personnel who are thoroughly familiar with color printing and typesetting; however, since few company printshops have suitable equipment, such work is usually done by vendors.

1.6 Summary of Functions

The functions of a typical technical publications department may be summarized as follows:

- Planning and editing technical publications, including

  Contractual reports

  Proposals and presentations

  Research studies

  Scientific papers

  Special brochures

  Development plans

  Activity reports

  Research memoranda

  Interoffice communications

  Articles for external publication

  Symposium proceedings

- Writing some of the publications listed above
- Writing technical manuals
- Writing on a regularly assigned basis for research and engineering organizations
- Preparing and periodically revising biographies of technical personnel
- Typing rough-draft material and reproduction copy
- Planning and preparing line and halftone illustrations for publications

- Preparing presentation charts
- Preparing slides for scientific meetings
- Maintaining slide files, chart files, and stock of negatives for black-and-white reproductions of charts
- Preparing programs and related items for symposia
- Providing photographic and printing support for the items listed above

Further details on the functions of technical publications departments are provided in Chapters 4 and 5, which describe the technical proposal and the technical manual.

Chapter 2
THE TECHNICAL PUBLICATIONS DEPARTMENT IN OPERATION *

2.1 Preliminary Procedures

Before a scientist or engineer begins writing a technical document, need for such a document must exist. This need may arise in any of several ways. A contract or a purchase request (PR) may call for a document. Need may also arise as a result of a particular set of military, political, or sales circumstances. There are many other possibilities.

Once the need is established, the management officer who will undertake the project assigns specific responsibility to the appropriate technical personnel. These persons should then confer with the technical publications department, where a decision will determine whether the preparation of the document requires technical writers or technical editors. Assignments are based on the amount of time and the number of people available for preparation of the document.

During the planning conferences, adequate budgetary support for the project is established. From this point on, teamwork between the scientific and engineering personnel and the members of the technical publications department is necessarily very close.

Considerable care should be given to the distribution list. For a contractual publication, the list is usually specified in the contract. For a noncontractual report, the distribution list is compiled by the author and the editor in accordance with relevant company policies and directives. In the case of classified publications, distribution must be limited to persons with an established "need to know." All distribution lists should be complete so that reprinting of publications will not be necessary.

---

*For procedures relating to the technical manual, see Chapter 5.

In accordance with security regulations, the author is responsible for determining the security classification of the document or its parts. The technical writers and editors will point out anything that they believe has been improperly classified, but they cannot assume a responsibility that rests with the author. In the case of contractual reports, the classification is usually specified in the classification guide that accompanies the contract. Information from this guide may be obtained from cognizant company administrators or security officers.

2.2 Writing and Editing

In preparing documents based on information supplied by research scientists and engineers, a technical writer works closely with the research personnel on whom he depends for such information. After an outline has been worked out cooperatively in preliminary meetings, he must develop a carefully planned schedule for completing each phase of the writing task. Since he needs time to write competently and since he is dependent on the research personnel for basic information, both he and the research personnel must adhere to a realistic schedule. A truly fine publication cannot be produced if the writer does not have access to the information he needs when he needs it. Late or last-minute delivery of data and inaccessibility of research personnel make the production of first-class publications all but impossible.

While the manuscript is being written, or even during the outline stage, both technical writer and research personnel should devote considerable attention to planning the visual materials, or graphics, that will be used in communicating the many ideas that they consider significant.

Among the more common types of visual materials are graphs, block diagrams, pictorial representations, schematics, flow charts, isometrics, wiring diagrams, cross-sectional views, or exploded parts drawings. (For examples, see Chapter 8.) The particular type to be used is determined by the nature of the ideas to be communicated. The decision should be made as soon as possible so that the artists can be preparing the materials while the report itself is being written.

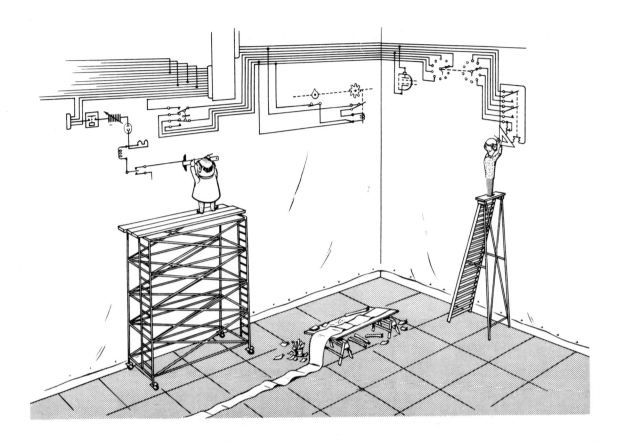

After the manuscript has been prepared, a technical writer proceeds in much the same manner as a technical editor, who has the responsibility for editing and producing a document from manuscript which has been prepared by research personnel and which he has helped to plan and outline. When a manuscript is given to an editor, his work is not confined to minor corrections in grammar, spelling, and punctuation. He also considers the manuscript from the viewpoint of the impact which it will make as a published document and proceeds accordingly. He looks for flaws in logic. He questions everything that he believes will not be clear to the intended reader, and, if possible, suggests changes in organization and wording that will make the meaning more exact. In sum, the editor is one of the first readers of the manuscript and is perhaps the most critical.

In this respect, the author should remember that the editor's criticism has one objective — to produce a publication which will reflect credit on both the author and the company. The author should consider the editor's comments very carefully, for the editor is one of the few readers to whom the author will have an opportunity to explain what he meant by what he has written.

After the manuscript has been edited, the editor goes over it line by line and paragraph by paragraph with the author. Suggested changes are agreed upon, and all corrections are made. The artwork is also carefully checked and corrected. At this stage (before final typing), if approval must be obtained from the author's supervisor or from some other company official, such approval must be obtained by the author. From this point on, the editor is responsible for all work until the manuscript is printed.

The editor submits the manuscript to the typists and helps to guide their work. After the final copy has been proofread by the typists, the editor reads it and has the necessary corrections made. In most cases, he sends the copy to the author for one last reading before it is printed. Lack of time in a highly compressed production schedule may prevent this step, but it is highly desirable and should certainly be undertaken if time permits. At this point, however, only minor changes, such as correction of any remaining typographical errors or misspellings, may be made. As in all other phases of the publication procedure, close cooperation between author and editor at press time ensures a smooth reproduction process and results in a publication of which both author and editor may be proud.

2.3 Summary

The sequence of steps in the preparation, production, and distribution of a technical publication is given in the following subsections.

2.3.1 Preliminary Steps

- Need for a document arises.
- Appropriate officer assigns responsibility to technical personnel.
- Technical personnel confer with technical publications department.
- Adequate budget is established.
- Security classification of the proposed publication is determined.
- Arrangements are made for preparing an appropriate distribution list.

2.3.2 Preparing the Manuscript

- Outline is prepared and agreed upon in planning conferences between technical personnel and technical writer or editor.
- Schedule for preparing the manuscript is established.
- Illustrations (halftones and line drawings, as described in Chapter 8) are agreed upon: Photographs are selected, rough artwork sketches are made, and the cover is prepared.
- First draft of the manuscript is written.
- First draft is reviewed by technical colleagues if there is sufficient time.
- Second draft is written if time permits.
- Editor obtains company document number.

2.3.3 Redrafting and Revising the Manuscript

- Rough sketches of the artwork are edited simultaneously with the writing of the first draft of the manuscript.
- Manuscript is edited.
- Editor and author confer on changes suggested by the editor.
- Editor and author confer on captions for the illustrations.

2.3.4 Preparing the Final Copy

- Editor gives the manuscript to the technical typing group for typing the reproduction copy (plates, bond, or vellum).
- Editor proofreads* the final copy and has the necessary corrections made.
- Editor gives the reproduction copy and the completed artwork to the author for final check and approval before printing.
- Editor submits tone illustrations (e.g., photographs), together with applicable captions, company document number, and page numbers, to photoshop where photoplates are made.
- Editor submits size-for-size line illustrations to printshop, together with captions and figure, page, and company document numbers, to be xeroxed onto paper plates.
- Editor submits large-size line illustrations to printshop for reduction by xerography** onto vellum.
- Editor has captions, as well as the figure, page, and company document numbers, typed on the Xerox vellums, which he then resubmits for xeroxing onto paper plates.

---

*Proofreading marks are shown in Appendix C. For offset reproduction, the marks are made in special nonreproducing colors: in light blue, when bond or vellum is used; and in brown, when a paper plate is used. For Ozalid or Copyflo reproduction, proofreading marks should be made on an overlay tissue, not on the reproduction copy.

**Xerography is a photolike process that reproduces images through the electrostatic transfer of a powder from a metal plate to the surface of the printing plate. Each page of copy is placed before a camera which focuses the image upon an electrically charged selenium plate. (The camera can reduce 50 percent or enlarge as much as 150 percent.) The image is recorded on the exposed selenium plate as an electrostatic charge distribution, rather than as a chemical change in an exposed photographic plate. The exposed selenium plate is developed with carbon powder, which the charge attracts to the plate to form the latent image. A paper plate is carefully placed in contact with the exposed selenium plate and smoothed into place. Next, the two are inserted into an electric field for a few seconds to transfer the image onto the paper plate. The latter is then carefully peeled from the selenium plate, and the powdered image fused to it by heating. Only a few minutes are required to prepare a paper plate from a typed sheet by xerography.

2.3.5 Printing and Distributing the Publication

- Editor prepares dummy of the publication, indicating classification of each page.

- Editor submits final reproduction copy, plates, and instructions (printer's dummy) to printshop.
- Printed sheets are collated and bound.
- Editor checks the first bound copy and indicates whether the remaining copies can be released for distribution.
- Responsible person or department sends the distribution list to the distributing unit.

- Distributing unit distributes copies of the publication.
- If the publication is noncontractual and is to be distributed outside the company, the author must have it "released" for external distribution in accordance with established company procedures.

PART 2

TYPES OF TECHNICAL PUBLICATIONS

Chapter 3
THE TECHNICAL REPORT

3.1 Introduction

The purpose of the formal technical report has already been indicated in the Preface — to provide information on the results of a research project. The audience to whom this information is communicated was also considered in the Preface, as well as the need for a well-organized, clearly written document if the communication is to be effective. In Chapter 2, the procedures followed in the preparation, reproduction, and distribution of a technical publication were described in some detail. Consideration was given to such items as assignment of responsibility, planning conferences, and collaboration between author and editor.

In this chapter, the classification and designation, if any, of a report are briefly considered, and the elements common to any well-organized report are discussed.

Both contractual and noncontractual reports are considered. It should be remembered, however, that contracts may specify the content, organization, or format of a report. When there is conflict between contract specifications and the general comments of this chapter, the contract specifications take precedence.

The three major divisions of a formal technical report are as follows:

- Front matter
- Body
- Back matter

Unless specified otherwise in Chapters 4 and 5, the comments pertaining to the technical report are also applicable to the technical proposal and the technical manual.

A consolidated list of all parts of the three major divisions is given at the end of this chapter.

3.2 Classification and Designation

3.2.1 Military Classification

A classified report is reproduced on preprinted paper bearing the appropriate military classification in 1/4-inch letters. Individual pages of a report may have different classifications. In such instances, the pages are reproduced on paper with the applicable security markings. The covers, and hence the report itself when identified as a single document, bear the highest classification used within the report.

3.2.2 Private Data, or Company Confidential

Certain kinds of publications contain information which the originating company considers private; that is, the information is confidential in a nonmilitary sense. Employees who generate such material and those who must have access to it should employ appropriate safeguards to ensure that the information is not exposed to persons for whom it is not intended.

The decision to designate information as Private Data or Company Confidential is the responsibility of the originator of the document containing such information, his supervisory personnel, or both. This decision is usually made in accordance with established company policies or management directives. Because of the information it contains, a document bearing the Private Data designation may also require a Department of Defense security classification. Special document-control

procedures for the safeguarding of Private Data documents normally include reproduction on paper bearing appropriate markings, carefully controlled distribution,
and secure storage.

3.3 Front Matter

The front matter of a technical report consists of the following parts in the order
given. (Not all parts are required in a single report.)

- Front cover
- Frontispiece
- Title page
- Special notice(s)
- Foreword or Preface
- Abstract
- Summary
- Acknowledgment(s)
- Contents (table of)
- Illustrations (list of)
- Tables (list of)
- Notation

3.3.1 Front Cover

The front cover of a technical report contains the basic information necessary to
identify the report. This information is so displayed typographically that the cover
is physically attractive. The cover should include the following items:

- Title
- Company document number
- Date
- Company imprint
- Classification, if any, at top and bottom

Many companies use a preprinted cover stock which includes the company imprint and a standardized design. Report title, date, and other necessary information are printed on the preprinted cover stock when a report is published. Designs and content for covers and title pages are often specified by contract.

3.3.2 Title Page

The title page of a report includes the same information as the front cover. In addition, it includes the contract number, if any, under which the report is produced; the name of the authors; and, if appropriate, the organizations of the authors.

In the case of a classified publication, the copy number, the number of sheets, and any other document-control information that is required are included on the title page. In addition, the title page of a classified publication includes the espionage clause, which reads as follows:

> This document contains information affecting the national defense of the United States within the meaning of the Espionage Laws, Title 18, U.S.C., Sec. 793 and 794. Its transmission or the revelation of its contents in any manner to an unauthorized person is prohibited by law.

3.3.3 Special Notices

Special notices often are included in technical reports because of company policy or contractual requirements. One kind of special notice is the proprietary notice of which there are two types — one for certain contractual reports and another for noncontractual reports, unsolicited proposals, and similar documents. The proprietary notice for certain contractual reports is specified in ASPR (Armed Services Procurement Regulations); if this notice is required, it must be used exactly as quoted. The other proprietary notice may be modified in accordance with the desires of company legal departments. It is common practice to include the proprietary-data notice in the front matter.

The proprietary-data notice for contractual reports is used only in reports generated under government contracts that contain paragraph (j) from ASPR 9.203.3. It should not be used unless requested by the contract administrator and approved by the legal department. The clause reads as follows:

> NOTICE: Furnished under United States Government Contract [appropriate contract number] and only those portions hereof which are marked (for example, by circling, underscoring, or otherwise) and indicated as being subject to this legend shall not be released outside the Government (except to foreign governments, subject to these same limitations) nor be disclosed, used, or duplicated for procurement or manufacturing purposes, except as otherwise authorized by contract, without the permission of [name of originating company]. This legend shall be marked on any reproduction hereof in whole or in part.

The proprietary-data notice for noncontractual reports, unsolicited proposals, and similar documents is as follows:

> PROPRIETARY DATA: The information and design disclosed herein were originated by and are the property of [name of originating company]. [Name of originating company] reserves all patent, proprietary, design, manufacturing, reproduction, use, and sales rights hereto, and to any article disclosed herein, except to the extent rights are expressly granted to others. The foregoing does not apply to vendor proprietary parts.

3.3.4 Foreword or Preface

The foreword or preface of a technical report normally states why the publication was produced and gives the contract number as well as the contract title under which the document is being submitted. It may also include the name of the customer (or sponsoring agency) and any other information that might be useful to either the contractor or the agency in determining exactly where the publication fits into a particular research program. If desired, the department or persons responsible for preparing the publication are identified. If necessary, the signature of the person responsible for approving the report is included.

The foreword or preface may also point out some of the features of the report and may acknowledge the efforts of individuals who contributed to the work associated with the publication.

In a technical report produced under government or military auspices, the title Foreword is used. In a commercial or nontechnical publication, Preface is used; or both Preface and Foreword may be included. In the latter case, the usual type of information is presented in the Preface, and the Foreword consists of a commendatory message from a person who is likely to be well known to the readers of the publication.

3.3.5 Abstract

An abstract indicates the subject matter and scope of a report. It contains enough information about the work reported on to satisfy the needs of a research worker who is seeking source material or of an administrator who is looking for a brief explanation.

Abstracts are of two types: descriptive and informative. A descriptive abstract merely announces or suggests what is to be found in the publication; it does not report or reproduce actual content. It is usually written in passive rather than active voice, as "An ingenious method of determining...is described. Four diagrams and six photographs are included." An informative abstract, as its name implies, transmits considerably more specific information than a descriptive abstract. In succinct form, it usually includes the important points made in the body of the report as well as other significant information. Unlike the descriptive abstract, an informative abstract normally includes the conclusions or recommendations stated in the report.

An abstract should be brief, but its length will depend on the size of the report. If possible, it should be brief enough to appear on a single page, but utmost care must be taken not to distort the facts in condensing. In addition, the abstract should be consistent in tone and emphasis with the parent report.

An abstract may be included in any technical report. It must be included: (1) if it is specified by contract; (2) if it is to be used as a separate document; or (3) if the report is also to appear as a research paper or article in a periodical.

3.3.6 Summary

A summary is longer and more comprehensive than a descriptive abstract. Like an informative abstract, it provides a brief survey of the why, what, and how of the research. It also states the conclusions and recommendations, if any. The summary is of particular value to persons who do not have time to read the entire report but who welcome succinct information on the purpose, method, results, and conclusions reported.

Every technical report, especially a contractual report, should have a summary or an abstract. Some reports contain both a summary and a descriptive abstract, which may be used as a separate document and may have a lower classification than the parent report.

3.3.7 Acknowledgments

Acknowledgments are expressed either in the foreword (or preface) or in a separate section after the summary. In research papers, the acknowledgments may be placed before the appendixes; however, placement before the table of contents is preferable when the technical publication is paginated by chapter (and appendix) and the front matter is numbered consecutively in lowercase Roman numerals. (See Chapter 6.)

In the acknowledgments, the author briefly thanks the individuals who contributed to the work described in the publication or to the production of the report. He expresses indebtedness to those whose contributions might otherwise not have been cited. Acknowledgments, however, are never used in lieu of identifying a writer-collaborator as an author. Nor are they used in place of footnotes or citations in the text to credit persons whose work is discussed or whose writing is quoted.

3.3.8 Table of Contents

On a contents page which contains subordinate headings, the chapter or section headings are typed in full capitals, and the subordinate headings are typed in initial capital and lowercase letters. Dependent on the size and complexity of a publication, secondary or second-order sideheads may be included. On a contents page which contains only chapter or section headings, the headings are typed in initial capital and lowercase letters. Page numbers are provided with each entry on a contents page.

3.3.9 List of Illustrations

When only a few illustrations are used in a technical report, a formal listing is not required; but with five or more, a list of illustrations is helpful to the organization of the report and to the reader. A list of illustrations includes figure numbers, captions, and page numbers, but usually does not include subcaptions and other explanatory material.

3.3.10 List of Tables

The criterion for a list of tables is basically the same as for a list of illustrations. Tables are listed with table numbers, titles, and page numbers. Subtitles, if any, are usually not included.

3.3.11 Notation

The formal listing of primary symbols used in a complex mathematical report is placed as a separate element immediately before the first section of the body of the report. The parts and format of this listing are described in Chapter 9.

3.4 Body

The body of a technical publication normally consists of the following parts:

- Introduction
- Discussion
- Conclusions
- References

3.4.1 Introduction

The introduction provides a setting for the publication. It includes background information on the problems under study, references to the past history of the project, and other material that will contribute to the reader's understanding of the subject matter. The introduction may be either detailed or condensed, depending on the requirements of the audience to whom the publication is addressed.

Appropriate titles or subtitles for the introduction might include one or more of the following:

- Background
- Early History
- Objectives
- Statement of the Problem
- Plan of the Report

3.4.2 Discussion

The discussion is the main part of the text. It may consist of a single section or of many sections, depending on the length and complexity of the publication. The various parts of the discussion are appropriately titled and might include the following:

- Instrumentation
- Equipment and Procedures
- Experimental Results
- Discussion

3.4.3 Conclusions

Not all technical reports require conclusions. When significant findings are reported, conclusions are a necessary part of a publication. Negative results or failure to obtain results should also be reported. Recommendations based on the results of a study may be included in the section presenting conclusions, or they may be placed in a separate section for reasons of length, emphasis, or contract specifications.

3.4.4 References

References are usually presented as the last section of the report, preceding appendixes, if any. In some reports, however, it may be convenient to list the references at the end of each section.

The list is titled <u>References</u> when it includes only the reports, books, and articles that are called out in the main body of the publication. The references are listed in the order in which they are cited in the text. When a list also includes references that have not been called out, it is divided into two sections, <u>Cited References</u> and <u>Uncited References</u>. If all references are uncited, the list is titled <u>Bibliography</u>; it may include items which relate to the subject under consideration but which were not consulted in the preparation of the report. (See also Chapter 10.)

3.5 Back Matter

The back matter may consist of:

- Appendixes
- Index
- Distribution list
- Back cover

3.5.1 Appendixes

Appendixes consist of material related to the report or of material which is considered too technical, detailed, or bulky to include in the body of the publication. Such material may be necessary to provide supporting evidence for some phase of the reported work. If included in the main text, however, it would disrupt the continuity and interfere with the orderly development of the thesis.

Tabular records of raw data, sample calculations, derivations, analytical procedures, and preliminary tests are examples of items considered appropriate to an appendix. Whatever the subject, the author must develop it fully but briefly as an aid to the reader. If the material does not meet the criterion of close and direct relationship to the subject matter of the publication, it should not be included in an appendix.

All appendixes should be called out in the text.

3.5.2 Index

An index contains references to significant topics included in the text and illustrations. Preparation of a good index requires considerable time and thought. Since most technical publications are produced on tight schedules, indexes can seldom be prepared within the time available.

3.5.3 Distribution List

A distribution list must be included in a contractual report if specified by the contract. It is supplied to the technical publications department before the report is reproduced. A distribution list is normally not included in a noncontractual report.

3.5.4 Back Cover

If a document is classified, the classification given on the front cover is repeated at the top and bottom of the back cover.

3.6 Sequence of Parts

For convenience, the proper sequence of all parts of the major divisions discussed in this chapter is shown in the following list:

- Front matter
    - Front cover
    - Frontispiece
    - Title page
    - Special notice(s)
    - Foreword
    - Preface
    - Abstract
    - Summary
    - Acknowledgment(s)
    - Contents (table of)
    - Illustrations (list of)
    - Tables (list of)
    - Notation
- Body
    - Introduction
    - Discussion
    - Conclusions
    - References
- Back matter
    - Appendixes
    - Index
    - Distribution list
    - Back cover

Chapter 4
THE TECHNICAL PROPOSAL

4.1 Introduction

A technical proposal is a publication designed to display ability to undertake a particular project and to carry it to a successful conclusion. A technical proposal is therefore a selling document. Frequently it sells ideas and capabilities relating to an end product which does not exist at the time that the proposal is submitted.

Proposals may be made for such projects as research studies, development of single hardware items or entire weapon systems, feasibility studies, computer solutions, and data evaluations. Basically, however, the common purpose of all proposals.is to persuade the persons to whom they are addressed — the audience — that the bidder can do a certain job and can do it better than any other organization. Consequently, proposals must provide information which the audience can use in making sound decisions.

4.2 Proposal Categories

4.2.1 Solicited Proposal

As a result of the tremendous expansion of the research, development, and manufacturing effort in recent years, and associated increases in cost, the contracting agencies evaluate much more critically the capabilities of prospective contractors and subcontractors. Not many years ago, a bidder had to submit little more than an estimate of the cost of performing the proposed effort. Today, the customer demands much more information. He wants to know how the bidder plans to approach the technical problem; how he expects to accomplish the work; what pertinent capabilities, experience, facilities, and equipment he possesses; how much the effort will cost; and what schedule he will follow.

To obtain this information, the customer issues invitations to a number of organizations which are considered competent in the technical field concerned. Such an invitation is called a Request for Proposal (RFP) or a Request for Quotation (RFQ).* The invitation presents in detail the technical requirements for the work to be accomplished and may even specify an outline for presentation of the required information. The publication which is prepared by a recipient of the invitation and submitted to the prospective customer is a solicited proposal.

---

*Hereafter, the invitation is referred to as the RFP.

4.2.2 Unsolicited Proposal

A second category of proposal is self-initiated and is known as an unsolicited proposal. Such a proposal is prepared when an organization believes that study of a particular problem area is desirable or necessary and that the results would warrant "outside" financing; or when an organization learns informally of the desirability of submitting a proposal for work in a specific field.

4.2.3 Technical Brochure

The technical brochure may be considered another type of technical proposal. A brochure is essentially a general proposal. It may describe the capabilities of a company or department in terms of background, experience, operations, facilities, and equipment. It may also be used to present a particular technical program, a system concept, a newly developed device, or a special service. In effect, the technical brochure is a proposal that presents a capability or program to the customer in terms of his present or potential need for research, development, equipment, or service. Figure 4-1 shows the cover of a representative technical brochure. Since a brochure is usually directed toward a varied audience and is intended to serve a promotional purpose, it embodies a dignified promotional text, a special and individualized format, and unusual color and design treatment.

Standard format cannot be specified for a technical brochure. The particular purpose involved, the layout, type, and art treatment desired or necessary, and the important element of cost are factors that make each technical brochure a highly individualized effort.

When a brochure is being planned, the editor should confer with the responsible technical staff member to establish the following guidelines:

- The specific purpose of the brochure
- The audience to whom it is directed

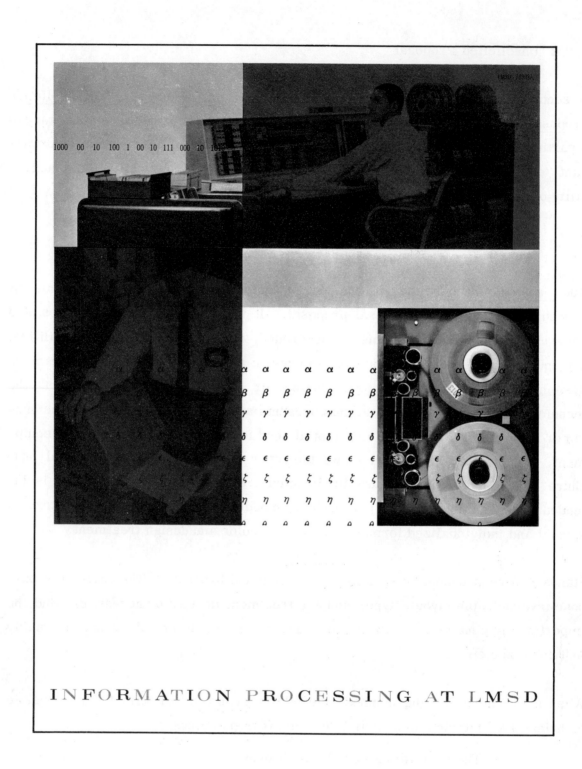

Fig. 4-1 Typical Cover of a Technical Brochure

- An outline of the proposed content
- A mutual understanding regarding general style and format, authorized expenditure, and time available
- The specific security classification of text and illustration input

The kind of preliminary presentation needed for review purposes (rough layout, rough comprehensive, or detailed comprehensive) must be determined before final artwork is started and the copy prepared for printing. Availability of internal or external printing facilities must also be determined, and use of typewritten or typeset text must be decided.

A technical staff member should be assigned to provide final technical approval at the working level for text and illustrations. Contact between the editor and several contributing technical personnel may be necessary during development of the material; however, one person should be clearly responsible for providing the editor with firm approval of the material, for helping with the maintenance of a consistent approach and treatment for the various sections of the brochure, and for resolving any problems that may develop.

The required approvals (e.g., organization management, sales or marketing, public relations, and top management) should be based on the preliminary text and layout to avoid costly and time-consuming revisions.

4.3 The Audience

The audience to whom a technical proposal is directed usually consists of the proposal reviewers at a particular government agency or industrial organization. The reviewers are military or civilian personnel representing a broad range of background and experience. These reviewers comprise three major groups:

- Senior scientists who have technical experience and up-to-the-minute awareness of the state-of-the-art in the technical area with which the proposal is concerned

- Technical specialists who have extensive experience and knowledge of particular aspects of the technical area with which the proposal is concerned
- Administrative specialists who are usually directly concerned with the cost and schedule of the proposed program

This audience must be kept in mind during all phases of preparation of a proposal. Essentially, a twofold question must be considered: "What does the reviewer already know, and what must he be told to be convinced that his agency will be best served by awarding this contract to this particular bidder?"

In some instances, proposals are prepared for quite a different kind of reviewer. For example, proposals for extensive and complex overall strategic or tactical programs may be reviewed by high-level military or government officials. For this type of reviewer, the language, the illustrations, and the amount of detail provided may differ greatly from what is usually required.

4.4 General Format

4.4.1 Sequence

The preparation of a technical proposal requires a flexible approach to the selection of format and content. Typical considerations affecting this selection are the nature of the program or task concerned, the requirements of the RFP, and the relative emphasis to be placed on capabilities. Nevertheless, enough elements are common to most proposals to justify establishing a pattern of format and content for achieving the best presentation of the bidder's response to the RFP.

As with the technical report, the technical proposal is divided into three parts: the front matter, the body, and the back matter. The following list presents, in preferred sequence, the elements contained in each part. The elements which may not be required for a given proposal, depending upon its size, scope, content, or special character, are indicated by daggers. (A variation in sequence may be specified by the customer.)

- Front matter

    Front cover

    Frontispiece [†]

    Title page

    Proprietary notice(s)

    Foreword

    Contents (table of)

    Illustrations (list of) [†]

    Tables (list of)[†]

    Notation [†]

    Summary

- Body

    Introduction

    Statement of work

    Program organization [†]

    Discussion

    Qualifications

    References[†]

- Back matter

    Appendixes (including personnel resumés) [†]

    Distribution list[†]

    Back cover

4.4.2 Front Matter

<u>Front cover, frontispiece, and title page.</u> The format and content of the cover and title page are generally similar to those for reports and manuals. (See subsections 3.3.1 and 3.3.2.) However, the selling function of the technical proposal may justify the use of a specially illustrated cover (Fig. 4-2) and perhaps a frontispiece

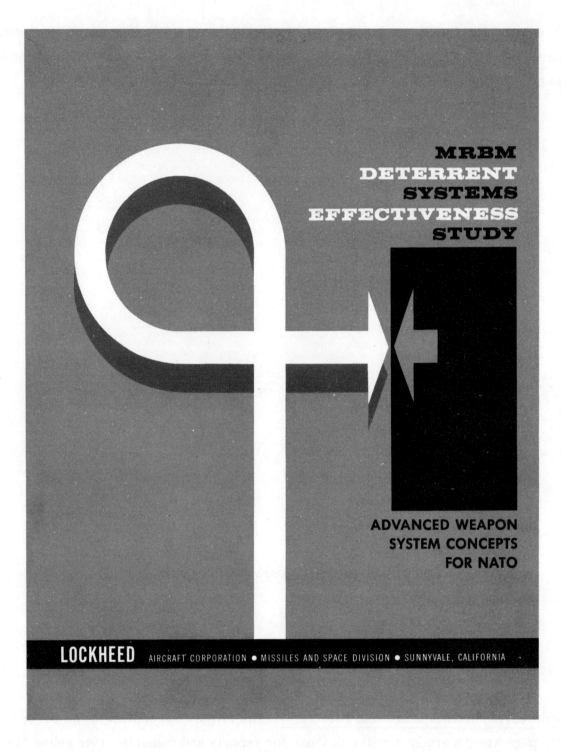

Fig. 4-2 Example of a Specially Illustrated Cover for a Technical Proposal

and a special title page. A special cover or a frontispiece is particularly desirable when the proposed program involves advanced design concepts. In such cases, the illustrated cover or frontispiece will assist the reviewers in visualizing the design concept and may also contribute significantly to the impact of the proposal. Occasionally, when the budget allows, an abstract or stylized art rendering of the subject matter is displayed on the cover, and a realistic rendering is presented by the frontispiece. Since illustrative covers and frontispieces are expensive and time-consuming to produce, their utility should be carefully evaluated.

Proprietary notices. Frequently, proposals must contain information, designs, concepts, descriptions of equipment, and illustrations of components or systems in which the bidder has a proprietary right or interest. To protect the bidder, a notice page which specifies such interest must be included in the proposal. Usually, the notice is placed on the reverse side of the title page, or on the page following the title page when the printing is on one side only.

The content of the proprietary notice varies with the nature and degree of protection that the bidder's legal staff considers necessary. However, government agencies require specific wording to protect technical reviewers and other government personnel against improper revelation of the content of the proposal. A typical proprietary notice for solicited proposals to the government is as follows:

> NOTICE: These data, furnished in response to [RFP or RFQ number] shall not be disclosed outside the Government or be duplicated, used, or disclosed in whole or in part for any purpose other than to evaluate the proposal, provided that if a contract is awarded to this offeror as a result of or in connection with the submission of such data, the Government shall have the right to duplicate, use, or disclose these data to the extent provided in the contract. This restriction does not limit the Government's right to use information contained in such data if it is obtained from another source.

In the case of solicited proposals to commercial organizations, the words the Government in the above proprietary notice are replaced by the name of the company to which the proposal is being submitted.

The proprietary notice for unsolicited proposals to a government agency is worded as follows:

> PROPRIETARY DATA: The information and design disclosed herein were originated by and are the property of [name of bidder]. [Name of bidder] reserves all patent, proprietary, design, manufacturing, reproduction, use, and sales rights hereto, and to any article disclosed herein, except to the extent rights are expressly granted to others. The foregoing does not apply to vendor proprietary parts.

In solicited proposals to government agencies, the appropriate proprietary data notice must also be placed on all text and illustration pages containing proprietary information. The notices are usually reduced in size and are either printed or stamped on the appropriate pages.

Foreword. The foreword is a brief statement, usually no more than half a page, which states the reason for submitting the proposal, the organization for which the proposal is intended, and the subject of the proposed program. For a solicited proposal, the identifying number and date of the RFP and the name of the source are included. For an unsolicited proposal, the reason why the submitting organization believes that the particular area warrants some type of effort should be briefly stated. If the size of the proposal requires publication in more than one volume, the foreword should make reference to the other volumes.

Contents (table of). See subsection 3.3.8.

Illustrations (list of). See subsection 3.3.9.

Tables (list of). See subsection 3.3.10.

Notation. See subsection 3.3.11.

Summary. The summary is a statement of the purposes, approaches, techniques, work to be done, pertinent qualifications, and anticipated results of the proposed technical effort. This section can make or break the proposal. It is read by more persons in positions of authority in customer organizations than any other part of the proposal; it facilitates technical review of the proposal; and it is particularly helpful to administrative or financial personnel who participate in awarding of contracts.

Generally, the summary is presented as a separate section preceding the introduction to the proposal. It should be brief in relation to the size of the proposal and should seldom exceed two pages. However, for very short proposals (20 pages or less), it may be more practical to incorporate the summary into the introduction. The summary must not present information which is not developed in the body of the proposal, nor should it be used as a device for avoiding preparation of a concise and carefully written proposal.

4.4.3 Body

Introduction. The introduction is one of the most important sections of the proposal. It provides the technical reviewer with his initial impression of the bidder's capabilities and may prejudice him favorably or unfavorably toward the entire proposal. It is essential, therefore, that the introduction be so concise, well organized, and clearly written that it leads the reader quickly and logically into the technical discussion which follows. It should not be cluttered with secondary details which belong in the discussion.

The introduction normally includes background information on the need for the proposed study. It states the objectives of the program, defines the major problems involved, indicates the major concepts underlying the proposed work, and describes the primary approaches to be explored. If appropriate, it may point out limitations in the proposed work and any other special considerations. If the program is extensive, it may also be desirable to list all the phases entailed.

Statement of work. The statement of work is a brief and direct summation of the work that the bidder will perform. It does not include technical details of why or how the work is to be done. A typical statement of work is shown in Fig. 4-3.

The statement of work may enumerate the theoretical studies, research investigations, or experimental laboratory work to be accomplished; or it may specify the equipment to be developed and fabricated and state the kinds of tests or evaluation efforts to be performed. It states whether the customer will receive data, hardware, or both and may indicate equipment delivery dates. It specifies the dates for any interim reports and may also contain a short paragraph describing the proposed work plan. If a program organization (page 4-14) is not included, this paragraph should be supplemented by a chart listing the various phases of the proposed effort and the amount of time to be devoted to each. (See Fig. 4-4.)

The statement of work serves the following purposes:

- It provides the technical reviewer with a checklist for comparing the program outlined in the proposal with the requirements contained in the RFP.
- It presents a descriptive itemization of the proposed work for comparison with the cost information accompanying the technical proposal.
- It is the bidder's commitment to perform the work specified and thus has the binding force of an actual contract.

The statement of work must be checked carefully to ensure that it specifies only those tasks that are included in the technical discussion.

For technical, cost, or other reasons, the bidder may not wish to commit himself to fulfilling all the requirements specified by the customer. In such instances, the specific deviations must be described briefly in the statement of work and should be supported in the technical discussion by a detailed explanation of the reasons for these deviations.

4-12

Section 2

STATEMENT OF WORK

As specified by RFP PR-120814, [name of bidder] will perform the following work according to the schedule presented in Fig. 4-4.

(1) Conduct studies of the basic equations proposed by Hamaker (Ref. 1) to provide specific solutions to be used in describing the transmittance, reflectance, and emittance of radiation by transparent and semitransparent layers at elevated temperatures. These studies will be accomplished by the following efforts:

- Mathematical analysis of the differential equations to find consistent analytical solutions in closed forms, in series forms, and as analytical approximations to both forms under isothermal conditions

- Computer programs based upon the laboratory determination of the optical parameters to be used for resolving the results of the foregoing mathematical analysis

- Development of useful empirical relationships of the absorption and scattering coefficients of polycrystalline materials and relating these data to the absorptance of single-crystal materials

(2) Design and fabricate the special apparatus required for determining the optical scattering and absorption characteristics of semitransparent materials

(3) Make experimental determination of the thermooptical parameters (emittance, reflectance, transmittance, absorptance, and scattering coefficients) of transparent, semitransparent, and translucent materials

(4) Prepare and transmit a summary technical report following completion of the proposed program

(5) Deliver to [name of customer], following termination of the program, the special equipment required for the proposed investigation, together with complete operating instructions

Fig. 4-3 Typical Statement of Work

Phase	1961							1962				
	Jun	Jul	Aug	Sep	Oct	Nov	Dec	Jan	Feb	Mar	Apr	May
Theory												
Analytical Studies												
Computer Effort												
Empirical Evaluation												
Equipment Order and Design												
Procurement and Buildup												
Experimental Determination of Thermooptical Parameters												
Calorimetric Determination of Thermal Parameter												
Final Effort												

Fig. 4-4 Typical Program Schedule

Program organization. Customer organizations, particularly government agencies, often require information about how the bidder will organize the proposed technical effort, what parts of the bidder's organization will be used, how the bidder will employ his various capabilities, and what schedule he proposes for the program.

In some proposals, this information constitutes a separate section of the proposal, usually after the statement of work. In short proposals, it may be included in the statement of work, following the list of tasks to be performed.

The text presentation of this information can be supplemented by a chart (Fig. 4-4) which clearly indicates the various tasks to be performed and which provides a schedule for these tasks. Organization charts are especially useful to indicate how the proposed effort will be organized and how it will fit into the bidder's established operational and management functions.

Discussion. The discussion contains the details of the proposed program and describes the technical approach, technical program, and development plan. It includes conceptual details, theoretical studies, experimental laboratory work, and development and evaluation tests, as well as descriptions of hardware, apparatus, procedures, and other applicable aspects of the work. If feasible, the anticipated results of the proposed program should be indicated. Any deviations from the requirements of the RFP should be explained in detail and clearly justified.

The various aspects of the program should be presented so that the technical reviewer can readily understand the nature and potential of the research or development. Preferably, the discussion should be divided into specifically titled sections rather than treated under one broad title such as Technical Discussion.

A positive approach should be taken in the discussion. Nevertheless, a difficult aspect or problem concerning the program should not be ignored, nor should there be any implication that a problem is simpler than those who are versed in the state-of-the-art know it to be. A difficulty should be presented as a problem which the bidder is confident he can solve or about which he can develop useful information for ultimate problem solution.

To impress a technical reviewer favorably, the discussion should be written as succinctly as possible without sacrificing essential detail. Although supporting data, formulas, and equations should be included when required, such material can often be summarized and supplemented in one or more appendixes with detailed descriptions, derivations, or tabulations. Use of appendixes often preserves the flow of the presentation and makes it easier for the technical reviewer to follow the line of development.

Bidder qualifications. In addition to providing a convincing technical presentation of the proposed effort, a proposal must contain a detailed description of the bidder's technical personnel, related experience, and pertinent facilities available for the program. These qualifications are carefully evaluated by the technical reviewers.

The experience and capabilities of the bidder's technical personnel constitute a significant basis for the award of a contract. Therefore, the proposal should contain a specific summary of the backgrounds and achievements of those who will be assigned to the program. Resumés of such personnel* should be presented in an appendix cited in the discussion. (See Fig. 4-5.) Care should be taken to avoid overloading the proposal with resumés of top-level personnel who will not actually participate in or directly supervise the project.

The bidder's successful experience in scientific or technological areas related to the proposed effort should be concisely presented so as to emphasize the bidder's

---

*The maintenance of up-to-date resumés in reproducible form (e.g., bond reproduction copy for xeroxing) for each technical staff member contributes to significant saving of time and effort. Bond masters also permit relatively easy revision of present duties and prior experience in order to emphasize the qualifications that are related to the proposed effort.

Richard James, Research Scientist

Nuclear Physics,
Spacecraft and Missiles Research

Conducts general research on low-
energy nuclear physics, using the
Van de Graaff accelerator.

EXPERIENCE

1958—LOCKHEED MISSILES AND SPACE COMPANY.
1958—59 Associate Research Scientist, Nuclear Physics.

1953—58 STANFORD UNIVERSITY, Stanford, Calif.
1957—58 Research Associate, Physics Department.
Performed pure research in the field of low-energy
nuclear physics, including nuclear polarization experiments and decay-scheme work.
1953—57 Research Assistant. Worked on gamma-ray
spectra from nuclear reactions produced by the Stanford
cyclotron. Designed scintillation-pair spectrometer to
be used with the cyclotron.

EDUCATION

Ph. D., Physics, 1958, Stanford University. Disser-
tation on gamma rays from deuteron reactions

B. S., Physics, 1953, Stanford University

SOCIETIES

American Physical Society
Society of the Sigma XI

PUBLICATIONS

"Recoil Ion Study of the $B^{11}(d,p)$ B^{12} Reaction," with
T. Ogo, Bull. Am. Phys. Soc., Ser. II, Vol. 2, 1957,
p. 388

"On the Levels of Be^{10} and B^{10}," with B. G. Hoffmeyer,
Phys. Rev., Vol. 3, 1958, p. 1216

Fig. 4-5 Typical Personnel Resumé

knowledge of pertinent problems, the state-of-the-art, and advanced techniques. Past or current programs and investigations that the bidder has undertaken should be briefly summarized. In some instances, specific contracts should be identified. When extensive or complicated programs are involved, attention should be called to the bidder's capabilities in program management and direction. The following program summary provides the kind of information desired:

> Satellite Systems Program. [Name of bidder] has been the prime contractor in an extensive satellite systems program in which it has directed the design and development of complete satellite systems with varied operational objectives. Included are the Discoverer and Midas systems. Flights conducted under this program have demonstrated capabilities for achieving various orbits, highly accurate in-orbit attitude control, stable flight response to ground-control signals, programmed ground-communication techniques, satellite recovery, and in-orbit restart. The program has also been marked by advanced results on data-gathering systems with special emphasis on photographic, electronic, and infrared techniques.

The technical reviewer is primarily interested in the specialized or unusual facilities or equipment that the bidder can provide for accomplishing the proposed program. Emphasis should be placed, therefore, on descriptions of equipment, laboratories, and buildings that are directly pertinent to the conduct of the work. For special items, complete information should be given on equipment capacity. The availability of standard laboratory or testing equipment may be indicated, but details of such equipment should not be included. If the proposed effort is extensive or highly complex, information on the bidder's overall facilities may also be warranted. Special facilities or equipment may be emphasized by photographs or drawings. Maps depicting the size, scope, and geographical relationship of facilities may also be useful.

References. The list of references is the final section of the body. (See subsection 3.4.4.) References for proposals are usually limited to those cited in the text.

4.4.4 Back Matter

Appendixes. Appendixes for proposals are generally prepared in the same format as that used for technical reports. (See subsection 3.5.1.) The appendix containing personnel resumés is usually placed as the last appendix in a proposal and is introduced by an appendix title page bearing an appropriate page number.

Back cover. The back cover of the proposal may be blank except for the appropriate security classification, or it may be printed to complement the front cover when special artwork is used.

4.5 Cost Information

The technical proposal normally does not include information regarding the cost estimates for the manhour effort, materials, special facilities, or special equipment for the proposed program. Such information is usually supplied to the customer in a separate document or in the covering correspondence.

Separation of cost information and technical information is considered desirable by most customers (particularly government agencies), because it assures evaluation of the technical presentation by the technical reviewers without the influence of cost considerations. It also permits concurrent review of the cost estimates by procurement, financial, or administrative personnel.

4.6 Editing

4.6.1 Editorial Objectives

The major purpose of editing technical proposals is to assure the preparation of a publication that will make a favorable impression on the reviewer. An appropriate tone, consistency in style and format, and an attractive presentation can be highly instrumental in establishing a positive reaction and in emphasizing the superiority of the bidder's program and qualifications over those of his competitors. Specifically, careful editorial treatment can contribute toward achievement of the following objectives:

- Presentation of the content in a logical manner, in conformance with customer requirements
- Inclusion of all necessary elements in complete and meaningful form
- Expression of ideas, concepts, and descriptions in clear, concise language, and elimination of excessive generalization, obscure statements, jargon or colloquialisms, extravagant terminology, and trite phrasing
- Assurance of consistency in style and format of text and illustrations
- Preparation of easily understood and well-executed illustrations

For a convincing presentation, the technical writing must be clear, concise, and informative. To produce good technical writing under the time pressures typical of proposal preparation, the proposal content must be logically organized and developed from the beginning of the proposal effort. Completion of the proposal to meet a tight deadline requires coordinated and concurrent effort by the proposal leader, the proposal editor, the art staff, and the reproduction facility.

4.6.2 Initial Editorial Participation

The technical publications department should be notified of a pending proposal immediately after the management decision to bid for a particular contract. The proposal editor should participate in the proposal planning and preparation from the beginning. The editor should be supplied with complete information on the proposal requirements (e.g., a copy of the RFP) and should be notified of all major meetings to plan and discuss the proposed program as it affects the content of the proposal. Attendance at such meetings will familiarize the editor with the scope of the program and enable him to make an early estimate of the nature and extent of the publications effort.

Through initial collaboration, the editor can assist the proposal leader in organizing the draft to meet the requirements of the RFP in the prevailing style and format of the bidder's organization. The editor can also obtain estimates of the number of text pages, the number and character of the illustrations, and information on any special format or art requirements.

4.6.3 Scheduling

Early establishment of a realistic schedule for completion of the writing and publications phases of proposal preparation is essential, since the proposal must be ready for transmittal in sufficient time to assure its receipt by the customer on or before the due date. No matter how superior a bidder's proposed program and proposal may be, late delivery can seriously hamper his chances of receiving the contract.

The proposal leader rightly considers that the technical contributions are the most important aspect of the total proposal effort. However, he frequently does not realize that the necessary study, organization, and writing must be completed in time to permit the technical publications department to edit, type, illustrate, proofread, and print. The editor should make the proposal leader aware of these requirements and should work out a practical schedule. Such scheduling will enable the proposal leader to expend maximum time on the technical effort.

Production time requirements for proposals vary according to the nature of the text (e.g., mathematics versus "straight text"), the level of quality and presentation planned, and the current or pending workload in typing, art, and reproduction. Typical realistic time requirements are as follows:

- Editing, proofreading, and miscellaneous functions for both text and illustrations: 1 to 2 hours per page
- Typing and typing corrections: 1/4 hour per page for straight text to 1 hour or more for solid mathematics (depending in part on the legibility of the copy)

- Artwork: 1 hour for a simple graph to many hours for complex schematics, special treatments, or color presentations
- Photography: 1 to 2 days for average halftones, depending on complexity and color requirements
- Offset reproduction: 2 to 5 days for most proposals, depending on length, workload, and printing requirements (e.g., amount of xeroxing, use of color, and number of foldouts)

Illustrations and complex tables should be delivered to the editor as early as possible so that they can be processed concurrently with the text. Expeditious delivery is particularly important in the case of large illustrations or tables requiring photographic reduction and in the case of photographs requiring halftone negatives and plates or color treatment.

4.6.4 Responsibilities of the Proposal Leader

The time pressures of proposal preparation require that the technical publications department have a flexible attitude toward the condition of the material submitted for processing. However, the proposal leader can avoid unnecessary and time-consuming editorial effort by making certain that the text and illustrative material are prepared in conformance with accepted standards: The text material should be submitted as a final draft typed double space on bond, with special care that portions containing handwritten mathematics be legible. Line drawings of pencil sketches should be submitted for the illustrations, and glossy prints or negatives should be submitted for the photographs.

The proposal leader should organize the text material in accordance with the format described in subsection 4.4. All illustrations, tables, and references should be called out in the text. The security classification must be indicated on all pages.

Illustrations should be clearly identified by a caption and should be numbered consecutively throughout the proposal, or chapter by chapter, in the order of initial callout in the text. If possible, line drawings and graphs should be of a size and scale that will allow direct tracing in order to avoid time-consuming replotting or reduction. Scales, scale titles, and callouts should be clearly indicated. Tables should be identified and numbered in a separate sequence; they should be typed double space or clearly written to facilitate editing and layout.

All referenced publications or documents should be numbered in the order of initial callout in the text. When only a few references are cited, they may be presented as footnotes. Complete identification of references should be provided, as indicated in Chapter 10.

4.6.5 Responsibilities of the Editor

When the proposal draft is received, the editor should first analyze its organization to verify that it meets the requirements of the RFP as well as the specified format and style. The statement of work should be studied by the editor so that he can be certain that the technical discussion includes all work the bidder proposes to perform and excludes any work commitment not detailed in the technical discussion. Any aspect required by the RFP that is not covered in the technical discussion should be fully explained.

It is particularly important that the tone and style of a technical proposal be forthright and factual. A specious, extravagant tone, or an obscure, pretentious style can prejudice the reviewer against a basically sound technical program. Although the proposal is a selling document, its promotional touch must be judicious and dignified; hyperbole has no place in a technical proposal. Proposal editing should emphasize the simple, direct statement in lieu of the long, involved, and heavily qualified sentence. Ideally, long and short sentences should be intermixed to prevent an effect of choppiness and incompleteness on the one hand and verbosity and confused thinking on the other.

Illustrations for proposals should be edited in accordance with the specifications detailed in Chapter 8. Because of the usual time pressures, the editor should guide the preparation of illustrations so that time-consuming reproduction processes are avoided. For example, if the necessary quality and effective presentation will be achieved, artwork should be prepared for reproduction by xerography rather than photography.

A proposal must be as accurate and complete as possible when submitted for reproduction since there is seldom an opportunity to make revisions or corrections after printing. The proposal leader should review the edited reproduction copy for content and classification before printing. If time permits, a review of the edited draft should be made by the proposal leader before the reproduction copy is prepared. The proposal editor should schedule this review of either the draft or the reproduction copy and be guided by the time available, the magnitude of editorial changes, and his own familiarity with the subject matter. After the copy has been submitted for reproduction, the editor may be responsible for the following duties:

- Followup to assure printing on schedule
- Final check of the printed publication before binding
- Followup to assure delivery to the organizational unit responsible for transmittal of the proposal to the customer and to the bidder's distribution unit
- Disposition of original art, negatives, and reproduction copy

Chapter 5
THE TECHNICAL MANUAL

5.1 Purpose

Equipment for which a technical manual is required may range from a small specialized unit to an entire weapon system. The manual describes the equipment; explains how to install, operate, troubleshoot, repair, and adjust it; and often includes detailed circuit analyses and tables of replaceable parts.

The preparation of technical manuals is a specialized task with many complicated ramifications. In a brief discussion, it is possible to mention only some of the most important aspects of the work.

5.2 Manual Specifications

Generally, the contract under which the equipment was developed or manufactured specifies the particular kind of manual required and the persons for whom it is intended.

Some manuals are written specifically for engineers; others are written for service personnel or individuals with limited technical background. In the latter case, the Armed Forces have been especially concerned that such manuals be accurate, clear, and concise, as well as complete and durable. As a result of long experience, the Armed Forces are convinced that the effectiveness and reliability of complex military equipment are directly proportional to the quality of the technical manuals. Consequently, they insist on compliance with their handbook specifications, even to the extent of refusing to accept equipment that is not accompanied by a satisfactory manual. Each branch of the Armed Forces has developed specifications which spell out the content, arrangement, type of treatment, artwork, typesetting, methods of reproduction, and even the paper stock to be used.

Handbook specifications and contractual requirements must necessarily prevail over any conflicting instructions in this Guide.

5.3 Cost Estimates

Long before a manual is written, its cost has usually been estimated in a quotation. All personnel concerned with proposals are cautioned not to submit quotations for manuals until they have consulted a qualified technical writer. At best, cost estimating for manuals is a tricky business, and ignorance of common pitfalls and of contingencies which must be written into quotations may lead to extensive financial losses or unrealistic commitments. A recent Aerospace Industries Association survey indicated that manuals for complex hardware cost approximately $200 per typeset page.

5.4 Manual Preparation

5.4.1 Assignment of Responsibility

Most technical manuals should be written by publications engineers. An exception is the very small manual, which does not exceed 25 or 30 typewritten pages and which is prepared without exact specifications for a nonmilitary customer. Manuals of this type can be written by design specialists at low cost. Larger manuals, especially those written to military specifications, can be prepared at minimum cost only by technical writers. Such manuals require the efficient application and coordination of specialized knowledge and skills. The professional technical writer, in doing this job, releases the design specialist from the writing task and helps him to concentrate on the type of work he knows and does best.

5.4.2 Plans and Schedules

Large manuals require careful planning. They must be delivered with the equipment. They must not be started too soon, or much of the work may have to be redone as a result of design changes. One small change, such as a change in the reference symbol of a variable resistor, may necessitate changes in the detailed circuit theory, operating instructions, tuning or adjustment procedures, trouble-shooting instructions, performance tests, exploded views, complete schematic, simplified schematic, photograph callouts, and wiring diagrams. To minimize the effect of these changes, the writing of the large manual should not be started until approximately half of the schematic diagrams have been released.

One of the most important aspects of planning is estimating the scope of the job in terms of manhours required to delivery time and making certain that necessary manpower is available. Allowance must be made for the time required for writing, editing, and artwork, as well as typesetting and printing. A reasonable "freeze date" must be fixed beyond which no new information or changes will be incorporated in the manual. A complete outline based on applicable specifications and the nature of the equipment must be drawn up. The work must then be divided among the technical writers so that each knows exactly what he is to do and the schedule he must follow. The schedule should be based on the anticipated release dates of the hardware components, not on the sequence of material in the manual.

In manual preparation, typing, artwork, typesetting, and printing must be as carefully scheduled as the writing. Moreover, in many cases, government agencies want to review and approve the manuscript before it is printed. Time required for this customer approval must therefore be included in the overall production schedule. If waivers in applicable specifications are desired, they should be obtained as early as possible.

5.4.3 Working Arrangements

The engineering organization having design cognizance over the equipment must be prepared to answer the technical writer's questions. These questions can be held to a minimum and the entire job expedited if an informal exchange among writers and engineers is accomplished at the very beginning. The writers can be integrated into the design effort by:

- Attending technical conferences and writing the minutes
- Helping to prepare unit and system test-and-performance specifications
- Helping to perform laboratory tests and prepare related reports
- Expediting the transformation of breadboard schematic sketches into complete schematic diagrams suitable for reproduction in manuals

It should be realized that the technical writer has an engineering or scientific background in addition to knowledge of publications requirements, and that the more familiar he becomes with the equipment itself, the more competent he will be to describe it. To obtain a quick and thorough familiarity, he should be encouraged to contribute to the design effort. Since part of his job is to write complete circuit analyses, a good technical writer may often exert a stimulating influence on engineers through his questions, and may suggest design changes that would simplify or improve the equipment.

5.4.4 Preparation of Artwork

Artwork for manuals is generally quite different from artwork for reports. Drawings may range from simplified schematics to large and complicated drawings, such as power-control circuit diagrams, intercabling diagrams, exploded views, and phantom views. Since the main objective of the manual is to help the user of the equipment to understand its operation and to service it quickly and efficiently, illustrations must be carefully planned.

Illustrations must also be planned to make reduction, placement, and reproduction conform to military handbook specifications. For example, it is essential to know in advance what the size of the printed illustration will be — whether one column, full page, foldout, or some other size. The artwork must be prepared in such a way that various requirements will be met when it is reduced and reproduced; e.g., parallel lines will be separated by not less than a specified amount, lettering will not be smaller than a specified minimum size, and lettering may be read from left to right without turning the manual more than 90 degrees clockwise.

Different branches of the Armed Forces have different policies on retouching and callouts on photographs. For example, the Signal Corps requires 100-percent retouching and callouts, but the Air Force does not. The technical writer must be thoroughly familiar with the requirements of the military service for which the manual is being prepared, and he must direct the artists accordingly. The technical writer must be held responsible for, and must have the authority to monitor, the quality of all the services he draws upon in preparing a manual. The Armed Forces will reject all work that does not meet specifications.

Electrical schematic diagrams should always show signal flow from left to right and voltage drops from top to bottom. Signal flow is usually indicated by a heavy line. Stages of circuits should be grouped together, and the function of each stage and circuit should be clearly shown. Crossovers should be held to a minimum, and connecting lines should be as short as possible. Engineers preparing schematic sketches should keep these points in mind, since a properly prepared sketch will save much layout time in the technical publications department.

5.4.5 Approval of Manuscript

The technical writer must be familiar with the steps required for obtaining customer approval of a manuscript and for reproducing the approved manual. These steps are not always the same; they differ from service to service and from one manual to another within a service. Usually they are specified in the contract. To meet deadlines, it may be necessary to obtain approvals and to reproduce the manual on a piecemeal basis.

5.5 Subcontracting

5.5.1 Preliminary Considerations

Sometimes it is necessary or expedient to use the services of a manuals subcontractor. Entire manuals may be subcontracted, or only the technical writing, artwork, or typing. In any case, before selecting a subcontractor, the responsible technical writer should first become familiar with the performance records, facilities, capabilities, and key personnel of several subcontractors. He should critically examine samples of the subcontractors' products which most closely resemble the work he plans to subcontract, and he should deal only with qualified subcontractors. The purchasing department generally expects the technical writer to evaluate subcontractors and to identify those who are reliable.

5.5.2 Bidders Conference

If the job is large, three to five qualified subcontractors should be invited to a bidders conference. The invitation to bid, however, should not be issued until the technical writer is prepared to present a clear, concise, and complete outline of his requirements. In addition, he must be prepared to explain what equipment, materials, and services he will and will not provide. He must be careful to convey the identical message to all the invited subcontractors, and he must be sure to make answers to subsequent questions available to all.

5.5.3 Working With Subcontractor

The technical writer's responsibilities and obligations do not end the moment his company signs a contract with the subcontractor. On the contrary, he should arrange for a timely flow of reliable information to the subcontractor, and he should monitor the progress of the work. If the job is large enough to involve other hardware manufacturers, handbook subcontractors, or both, the technical writer responsible for the overall program should monitor the progress of the entire job. He should check for completeness of coverage, adherence to specifications and schedules, information gaps, duplication, and uniformity of style and format. At the conclusion of the job, the technical writer should receive all of the original artwork and reproduction copy because this material may be needed for revisions to the manuals.

PART 3

FORMAT

Chapter 6
HEADINGS AND PAGINATION*

6.1 Organization by Divisions

A technical publication is logically organized; its divisions reflect its logical organization. The major divisions are presented as sections or chapters, and the parts within these major divisions are presented as subdivisions or as sub-subdivisions. Each part and subpart is given a title. The section is provided with a centerhead; the subdivision, with a primary or first-order sidehead; and the sub-subdivision, with a secondary or second-order sidehead.

Author and editor alike should guard against organizing beyond a sub-subdivision. A third-order sidehead can rarely be justified. Excessive breakdown can be avoided if the manuscript or outline is corrected. With a proper introduction, for example, the material in question can be presented as a listing. In other instances, a run-in sidehead may be used, with the text continued on the same line as the head.

If a publication is logically organized, the usual rule for outlining is observed: Division of any portion must result in a minimum of two subdivisions. Thus, if an author provides one second-order sidehead, he is committed to providing at least one additional second-order sidehead. If he cannot, he should eliminate the single second-order sidehead and change the primary first-order sidehead to include the secondary. For example, if the only second-order sidehead under Subcontractors is Facilities, the first-order sidehead might be changed to Subcontractor Facilities.

---

*Various aspects of the format described in this chapter are illustrated throughout this Guide. A typical page layout for typists is shown in Fig. 6-1.

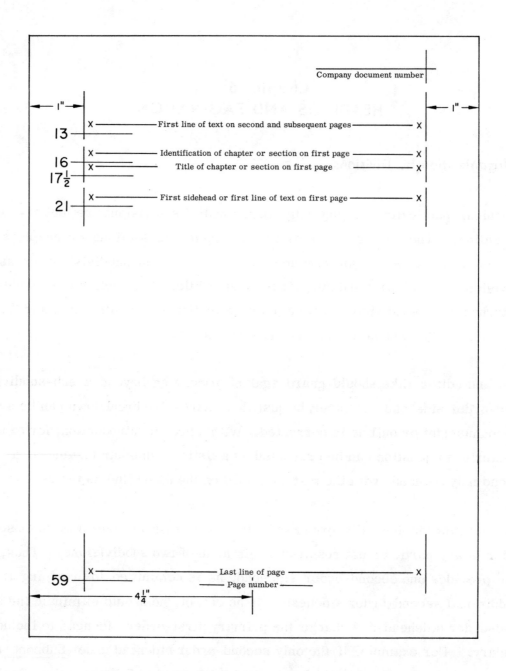

Fig. 6-1   Typical Page Layout for a Technical Publication.   Numerals refer to the number of spaces from the top of the vertical scale on the paper plates used in the offset printing process.   When standard-size bond masters are used, three fewer vertical spaces are required in each case

6.2 Presentation of Headings

6.2.1 Wording

The logical organization of the publication is reflected in the type of construction assigned to the titles and subtitles. Items that are parallel in thought are expressed in parallel construction. Thus, second-order sideheads are coequal in their function as subparts of a first-order sidehead. Under <u>Statement of Problem</u>, for example, it is inconsistent to express one heading as <u>Design Considerations</u> and another heading as <u>What Are the Environmental Factors?</u> Careful planning is readily evidenced by paralleling noun phrases.

6.2.2 Format

Block format is often used for technical publications. If a manuscript is also to be prepared for publication in a professional journal, the format of that journal may be used. Compliance with all requirements of the format will be assured if the author supplies the editor with the necessary information in ample time.

In the block format (as illustrated by this Guide), paragraphs are not indented even when materials belonging to subheads or sub-subheads are presented. In this Guide, 1-1/2 spaces are used between lines and 3 spaces are used to separate paragraphs and headings, whether primary or secondary.

The chapter (or section) identification consists of:

- <u>Chapter</u> followed by an Arabic numeral
- Title

Each appears on a separate line and is centered on the line. <u>Chapter</u> is typed in lowercase letters with an initial capital. The chapter title and the first-order sideheads appear in full capitals (all caps).

The second-order sideheads are typed in uppercase style (initial letters of important words capitalized). Although internal punctuation is used as required, no period is used after the chapter title or after the first- and second-order sideheads. Nor are any of these headings underscored.

A run-in sidehead is underscored. It is typed in lowercase style (only the initial letter of the first word capitalized). A period is used to separate it from the text which follows on the same line.

In special publications (such as this Guide), headings may be typed or typeset in various typefaces.

6.2.3 Numbering

Arabic numerals are used to identify the primary and secondary sideheads. Run-in heads are not numbered. The first-order sidehead is preceded by two numbers separated by a decimal point. The first number designates the chapter or section, and the second identifies the sequence of the primary heading within that chapter. The second-order sidehead requires three Arabic numerals and two separating decimal points. The first two numbers fulfill the same functions as those used with the first-order sidehead, and the third number identifies the sequence of the secondary sidehead within the primary.

6.3 Listings

Listings in text are usually preceded by a colon and are introduced by callouts such as the following or as follows. Such callouts are preferable to a colon immediately after are or some other form of the infinitive to be. Arabic numerals in parentheses, rather than lowercase letters, may be used to introduce the items in sequence, either continuously within the text or vertically in a column.

In column listings which are numbered, the items are indented. A greater indention is used for phrases than for sentences.* Unless the listed items are sentences (independent of the sentence which introduces them), no periods are used.

Noun or infinitive phrases are generally itemized, but not within the same listing, since the required parallelism in thought would be violated by the lack of parallelism in construction.

Bullets (filled-in o's) may be used in column listings when no reference is subsequently made to these items by numbers. The spacing is the same as for numbered listings. The device of bullet introductions lends attractiveness and variation to the format. In some instances, it even serves to emphasize the items under consideration. For example, the organizations within a company might be emphasized as follows:

- Research
- Weapon Systems
- General Services
- Space Systems
- Project Systems
- Manufacturing

---

*In this Guide, which was typed on a proportional-spacing typewriter, phrases are indented 32 units (10 spaces on a standard typewriter), and sentences are indented 16 units (5 spaces). Sublistings within a bullet are indented 10 units (3 spaces). Two vertical spaces are left between the first numbered item and the sentence which introduces the listing. The first letter of each listed item is capitalized, and the first word of each succeeding line of this item is placed flush with the first word of the opening line. In listings without examples, the normal 1-1/2 spaces are used between lines. In listings which have examples or notes, 2 spaces are left between the listed item and the example or note and before the next listed item. The normal 1-1/2 spaces are left between lines of the example, and between multiple examples which are less than half a line; 2 spaces are left between multiple examples which exceed half a line. Single spacing is used within each note.

6.4 Pagination

The pressure of deadlines often dictates the numbering of pages by chapter or section. Such a procedure also makes possible the addition or deletion of material with a minimum of repagination. In paginating by chapter, two Arabic numerals separated by a hyphen are centered at the bottom of the page, about 1 inch from the edge (Fig. 6-1). The first number identifies the chapter, and the second designates the sequence of the page within that chapter. When the report contains appendixes, the first Arabic numeral is replaced by the capital letter used to designate the particular appendix.

Front matter, beginning with the title page, is paginated with lowercase Roman numerals. Generally both sides of a sheet are printed, and the usual rule of pagination is observed: Right-hand pages are odd-numbered, and left-hand pages are even-numbered. For reasons of security and ease of identification, all pages of a company publication should bear a document number.

Chapter 7
TABLES

7.1 Purpose

Information that is readily grouped into classes or categories is usually best presented in a table. By the elimination of extraneous details and the orderly presentation of such information, trends can be emphasized and comparisons can readily be made.

Considerable flexibility is possible in constructing tables, since tabulation does not conform to rigid rules. However, two criteria govern all tabulations:

- A table must be a self-contained, self-explanatory unit.
- A table must be simple.

7.2 Types of Tables

Tables are classified on the basis of formats and of methods used in identifying them. The format of a table is closed if horizontal and vertical lines are used to separate the parts; the format is open if only the stub and column captions are underscored. A table that has an assigned title and table number is called a formal table. Every formal table is called out by number in the text immediately before the table is presented. A table is called a text table when it appears within the text, depends upon the text to disclose its identity, and has neither title nor number (page 7-7). Such a table is usually part of the sentence that identifies it.

Formal tables may have either open or closed format; text tables always have open format.

7.2.1 Formal Table

A formal table has two principal parts: the identification and the body. In addition, it may have a supplement. These parts are subdivided as follows:

- Identification
    Table number
    Title
    Subtitle
- Body
    Boxhead
    Stub
    Field
    Line and column designations
- Supplement
    Footnotes or reference lines

The parts and format of a formal table are illustrated in Fig. 7-1. Large formal tables are discussed on page 7-8.

As noted earlier, a formal table always has a number and title. Such identification is particularly essential if typing or spatial considerations make it necessary to separate the table from the page on which it is called out. Under such circumstances, it is desirable to refer to the table by number and to avoid such callouts as the following table or the table below.

When the system of pagination described on page 6-6 is used, tables are not numbered consecutively but in sequence by chapter or section. Two Arabic numerals separated by a hyphen are used to designate a particular table. The first numeral identifies the chapter; the second designates the number of the table within that chapter. For example, Table 2-4 indicates the fourth table in the second chapter.

Table 7-1

TABLE NOMENCLATURE[a]

(Space Allotment to Parts Is Determined by Page Size)

	Stub Caption	Column Caption	Multiple-Column Caption	
			Subcaption	Subcaption
	(1)	(2)	(3)	(4)
(1)	Line Heading...			
(1a)	Subheading..			
(1b)	Subheading..	Space for tabulated entries[b]		
(2)	Line Heading...			
(2a)	Subheading..			
(2b)	Subheading..			

(a) This table has a closed format.
(b) Space for individual entry is a cell.

Fig. 7-1 Parts and Format of a Formal Table

The title of the table should describe the material presented in the table clearly, concisely, and completely. The <u>what</u> of the tabular material is placed first in the title and is usually followed by the <u>where</u> and <u>when</u>, if this information is pertinent. Secondary information applicable to all material in the table but not essential for its identification is placed in a subtitle if its inclusion in the title would result in a long or awkward phrase. Secondary information includes units of measurement used throughout the table, general restrictions or limitations of the data, and sources of information.

In preparing a table, the word <u>Table</u> is typed in initial capital and lowercase letters, followed by the table number, and is centered above the table. The title appears two spaces below the table number and is typed in full capital letters. If a subtitle is required, it is centered two spaces below the main title and is typed in initial capital and lowercase letters. Both are punctuated internally, if necessary, but are not followed by periods. A subtitle, however, may be enclosed in parentheses.

The <u>boxhead</u>, the first part of the body of a table (Fig. 7-1), is the area in which the stub caption and column captions are placed. If necessary, a line of numbers in parentheses to designate the columns is included beneath the column headings. The boxhead lies within two horizontal lines; its captions are appropriately separated by vertical lines which extend through the other areas of the table. For quantities that have some feature in common, a multiple-column caption is used. A horizontal line separates this caption from its subcaptions.

The <u>stub</u> is the left-hand area that contains the line headings of a table. If necessary, it may have a column of numbers to designate the lines of the table. In line headings, the important words are typed in initial capital and lowercase letters. Line headings may be broken into two or more subheadings. In these subheadings, only the first letter of the first word is capitalized. Leaders (. . . . or - - - -) may be used to aid the eye in moving from the stub to the field of the table.

The field is the right-hand area in which the information is tabulated. The space in which an individual item is entered is called a cell. Each cell is formed by the intersection of the lines bounding a given line heading with those bounding a particular column caption.

To a large extent, appropriate wording and arrangement of the captions and line headings determine the effectiveness of a table. The stub caption must classify the line headings. The line headings in the stub column identify the entries in the cells. Each column must have a caption that concisely specifies the data appearing in it. Similarly, each line heading must precisely subdivide or classify the data in it. Grammatical parallelism should be maintained throughout the captions and line headings. Such parallelism may be easily achieved by the use of nouns or noun phrases for all headings.

Column captions are centered both vertically and horizontally in their boxes; periods are not placed after them. The abbreviation of the appropriate unit is always placed in parentheses just below the column caption. Powers of ten should be used in the column caption whenever possible. A column caption of the type $y \times 10^n$ indicates that the values of y appearing in the column have been multiplied by 10^n. If a caption must be placed broadside on the page because of its length, it must always be made to read from left to right, from the body of the table. If a single caption must be placed broadside in a table, all others should be similarly placed. Whenever possible, however, such placement should be avoided.

Line headings are usually aligned on the left within the stub. A line heading used to classify the data in several rows is centered within the space occupied by the rows and is not followed by a period. Subheads are slightly indented in the stub. Such headings as Total, Mean, and Average are always indented as subheads.

The sequence of both column captions and line headings should be logical. The arrangement may be alphabetical, chronological, operational, or quantitative. Column captions should read progressively from left to right.

The longest entry in tabulated written material is approximately centered in each column. Other entries within that column are typed flush left with the longest entry. Whole numbers are aligned on the right, and no decimal point is placed after them unless zeros must be added to indicate the degree of accuracy. Decimal numbers are aligned on the decimal point. A zero is always placed before the decimal point of a decimal fraction. If possible, a uniform degree of accuracy (i.e., the same number of decimal places) should be maintained in each column, but only as many digits should be used as the precision of the data justifies.

Double numbers (such as 6 ± 0.5, or 1,346 to 1,361) are aligned on the separating symbol; e.g., $\pm$, $-$, to, etc. A symbol that precedes a number ($+$, $-$, or $\pm$) is placed close to the number regardless of the alignment of the number. In a tabulated range of numerical values, to is preferable to the dash, particularly when the range includes decimals or operational signs.

Omitted or missing data are indicated by the word None or by a dash centered in the cell. (See page 12-12.) Generally, no cells are left blank, and zeros are used only to indicate quantitative values. Ditto marks are never used in a table.

The supplement of a table consists of footnotes or reference lines which supply auxiliary information about specific entries or which explain certain features of the table. Numbers and abbreviations are used as much as possible. The supplement is placed immediately below the table and is singlespaced. It is not separated from the table by text material.

Reference to a footnote is indicated in the table by a lowercase letter placed in parentheses as a superscript to the right of the entry. Such superscripts are consecutively lettered, beginning with the title, proceeding from left to right through the stub caption, column captions, and line headings.

7.2.2 Text Table

The text table has neither title nor number and rarely has a supplement. Its body is simple, consisting only of a stub and one to three columns. It is considered part of the sentence in which it is identified.

The stub caption and column captions are underscored in the text table. The appropriate unit is placed in parentheses beneath each column caption, if it is not explicitly stated in the identifying sentence. Leaders may be used in the text table to aid the eye. The following example illustrates the correct form for a text table.

A weight distribution chart for the payload is as follows:

Component	Number	Unit Weight (lb)	Total Weight (lb)
Angular Distribution Detector	2	8	16
Magnetic Spectrometer	2	8	16
Electronic Packages	4	5	20
Battery Packages	4	3	12
Integrating Dosimeter	1	0.25	0.25
Nuclear Emulsions	2	12	24
Diffraction Camera	1	2	2
Absorption Spectrometer	1	1	1
Radiation Survey Film	4	0.125	0.50
Total			91.75

7.3 Large Tables

A standard page provides two possible placements for a table:

- Normal, in which the column rulings run parallel to the length of the page (Fig. 7-2)
- Broadside, or twist, in which they run parallel to its width (Fig. 7-3)

The broadside position permits a table to have a few more columns than it could have in the normal position. However, the columns of such a table are shorter than the normal ones. To prepare a broadside table, the page is rotated 90 degrees. In this position, the number and title of the table always run parallel to the binding edge of the page. On a page containing a broadside table, the page number and the company document number are in the regular position, as though the page had not been rotated.

Both normal and broadside tables frequently require more than a single page. In such cases, the table number followed by the abbreviation Cont. in parentheses should appear on the second and subsequent pages. In a continued table, the box-head is repeated. The title, however, is not repeated.

A table too large for placement on standard-size paper may be prepared on a large sheet and (1) printed as a foldout or (2) reduced by xerography or photography and printed as a standard-size page. Another possibility is division of the large table into two parts, typed in broadside position on standard-size paper (or on large sheets and reduced), and presented on facing pages of the publication. In this case, the identification and the boxhead are not repeated on the second page.

Table 3-4

TYPES OF CATCHERS

Type	Designation	Diameter (in.)	Length (in.)	Drawing No. (a)	Quantity
Straight	I-1	2	17-1/2	1089670	2
	I-2	2	17-1/2	1089671	2
	I-3	2	17-1/2	1089681	7
	I-4	2	24	1089693	4
	I-5	2	36-1/2	1089528	4
	I-6	4	24	1089683	16
	I-7	4	24	1089673	1
Bottleneck	II-1	2	17-1/2	1089672	1
	II-2	2	17-1/2	1089682	11
	II-3	2	24	1089692	7
	II-4	2	27	1089687	44
	II-5	4	30	1089674	1
	II-6	4	30	1089684	5
	II-7	6	30	1089686	2
Self-closing	III-1	2	17-1/2	1089569	22
	III-2	2	17-1/2	1089677	41
	III-3	2	17-1/2	1089678	17
	III-4	2	17-1/2	1089679	14
Box	IV-1	2	—	1089704	1
	IV-2	2	—	1089705	1
	IV-3	2	—	1089706	1

(a) These drawings are contained in Appendix B.

Fig. 7-2 Typical Table Placed in the Normal Position

Table 7-8

CHARACTERISTICS OF CERTAIN REACTORS

Characteristics	Units	PWR (APPR-1)	BWR (EBWR)	SGR (SRE)	Fast (EBR-2)	Homogeneous (HRT)	Gas-Cooled (C-H)
Total Power	kw	10	20	20	60	5	3.6×10^5
Design Pressure	psia	1,600	800	~15	~15	2,000	~100
Test Pressure	psia	2,400	1,200	—	900	2,800	—
Coolant Exit Temperature	°F	450	488	960	900	570	637
Fuel Element Maximum Surface Temperature	°F	550	645	>960	>950	570	~767
Maximum Heat Flux	10^5 Btu/hr-ft^2	2.2	1.4	3.4	>7.5	—	—
Maximum Neutron Flux	10^{13} nv	10	2.4	6	250°F	—	—
Temperature Coefficient of Reactivity	10^{-5}/°F	-23	-1.9	-0.7	-4.5	-111	—
Prompt Neutron Lifetime	10^{-5} sec	2	6.3	—	—	—	—
Burnup	%	~25	—	~12.5	~4	—	—
Refuel Cycle Time	Months	18	—	10	3	Continuous	—
Maximum Credible Release of FP (10 sec after shutdown)	Curies	$~8.3 \times 10^4$	—	$~1.6 \times 10^5$	—	—	—
Average Scram Time	sec	0.53	0.35	—	—	—	—
Moderator Medium	—	H_2O	H_2O	Graphite	None	D_2O (Fuel)	Graphite
Coolant (Primary)	—	H_2O	H_2O	Na	NaK	(Fuel)	CO_2
Coolant Circulation	—	Forced	Natural	Forced	Forced	Forced	Forced
Control Element Medium	—	B_4C-Fe	Hf-B-Fe	B-Ni-Fe	Voids	Fuel conc.	B-Fe
Control Rod Configuration	—	~3" square	1/4" cross	2.3" diam. cylinder	—	—	Rod
Control Rod Length (Travel)	ft	~4	~4	~6	—	—	—
Fuel Element Configuration	—	Plate	Plate	3/4" diam. rod	Pin	Solution	U
Fuel Element Composition	—	UO_2-B_4C	U-Zr-Nb	U	U	UO_2SO_4	U
Fuel Enrichment	%	93	1.4	2.8	45	90	Natural
Fuel Cladding	—	304L-SS	Zircaloy-2	304 SS	SS	None	Mg alloy
Fuel Element Length (Total)	ft	~2	~4	6	—	—	~21 (1.15" diam. × 3.33 ft)
Spent Fuel Storage Well	—	Concrete	Concrete	SS-concrete	SS-concrete	—	Concrete
Spent Fuel Storage Fluid	—	H_2O	H_2O	Na	Na	—	H_2O
Primary Container Shape	—	Cylinder	Cylinder	Cylinder	Cylinder	Sphere	Cylinder
Primary Container Diameter	ft	4	7	~11	~10	2.67	37
Primary Container Thickness	in.	2.75	2.25	1.5	—	0.31	2
Primary Container Height	ft	13.5	~23	19	13	—	~60
Primary Container Material	—	Steel	Steel	304 SS	—	Zircaloy	Steel
Primary Container Cladding	—	1/4" SS	1/9" SS	None	—	None	—
Secondary Container Shape	—	Cylinder	Cylinder	Cylinder	—	Sphere	—
Secondary Container Diameter	ft	36	80	12.5	—	5	—
Secondary Container Thickness	in.	~24	1/4	1/4	—	4.4	—
Secondary Container Height	ft	64	119	19	—	—	—
Secondary Container Material	—	Steel-concrete	Steel-concrete	Steel	Yes	Steel-SS	—
Blast Shield	No	Yes	Yes	Yes	Yes	Yes	Yes

PWR   Pressurized Water Reactor
APPR   Army Package Power Reactor
BWR   Boiling Water Reactor

EBWR   Experimental Boiling Water Reactor
SGR   Sodium Graphite Reactor
SRE   Sodium Reactor Experiment

EBR   Experimental Breeder Reactor
HRT   Homogeneous Reactor Test
C-H   Calder-Hall Reactor (English)

FP   Fission Product
SS   Stainless Steel

Fig. 7-3 Typical Large Table Requiring Placement in the Broadside or Twist Position

Chapter 8
ILLUSTRATIONS *

8.1 Purpose

Illustrations are used in a technical publication to supplement the text. They may show detail that is difficult to describe in words. They may depict functional relationships between variables or make it possible to compare different sets of observations. Because they are expensive to produce, illustrations should not be used in a technical publication purely for decorative purposes.

The author and the technical writer or editor are jointly responsible for the illustrations in a technical publication. Together they must carefully consider each potential illustration, since only those which definitely assist the reader in understanding the text should be included.

8.2 Types of Illustrations

Illustrations used in technical publications are of two general types — line and halftone. Examples of each type have been cited in Chapters 2 and 5: Black-and-white graphs, diagrams, maps, and schematics are examples of line illustrations; photographs and airbrush drawings are examples of halftone illustrations. In the preparation and printing of the two types, the line illustration is generally less expensive and less time-consuming. To reproduce the halftone illustration, more complicated processes are required.

---

*For information on illustrations used in technical manuals, see Chapter 5.

8.2.1 Line Illustrations

The line illustrations submitted by an author consist typically of rough sketches and graphs. The author should carefully review the original illustrations and, in conference with the technical writer or editor, should explicitly direct attention to the features which he wants the technical artist to show. When possible, he should submit a photograph or production drawing to assist the illustrator in understanding the sketches.

Although the author is not restricted to using paper of a specific size, the artist's work is greatly simplified if graphs are plotted on standard graph paper, 8-1/2 by 11 inches. Unless explicitly directed otherwise, the artist will use ticks to indicate the grids.

Legends, callouts, and other text matter on a line illustration must be legible. Subscripts, superscripts, and Greek letters should be clearly designated. Most callouts are written in full capitals, including the units which are normally abbreviated in lowercase. (See the list given in Chapter 15.) The lowercase form is retained on callouts only when the abbreviation ordinarily consists of both capital and lowercase letters (e.g., Mc) to avoid confusion with the abbreviation for another unit (e.g., mC). On callouts it is permissible to use symbols for percent, feet, inches, and degrees.

In preparing graphs, the following information must be supplied for the variable plotted on each axis:

- Name or title
- Symbol (if any) used in the text
- Unit in abbreviated form

For each illustration, the author must also include the following:

- Figure number
- Caption
- Security classification

Figures 8-1 through 8-7 are examples of different types of line illustrations. If time permits, effective exposition may be achieved by placing a figure on the same page with the text. An example follows.

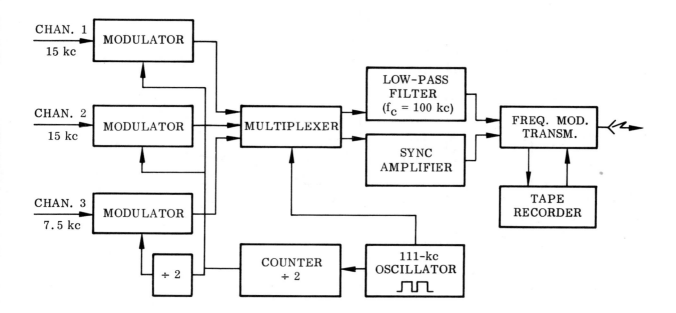

Fig. 8-1 Line Illustration: Block Diagram, Typewritten Callouts

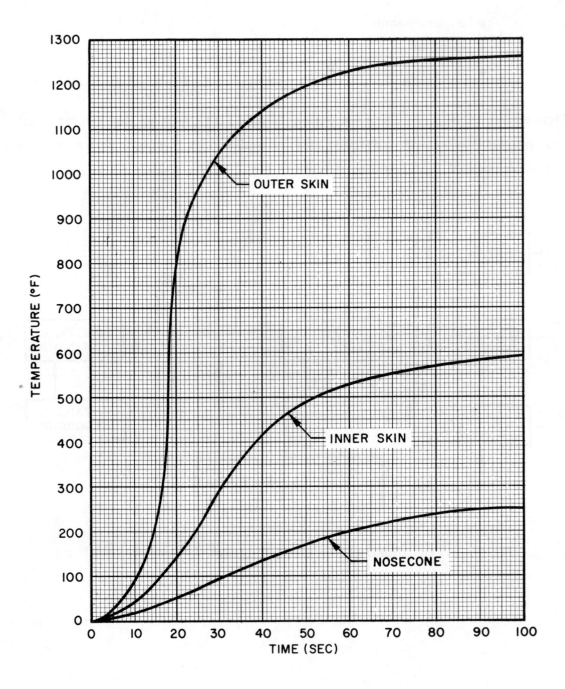

Fig. 8-2a Line Illustration: Graph With Many Fine Grids, Leroy Call-
          outs.   This kind of illustration is used when detailed and pre-
          cise information is to be read from the graph

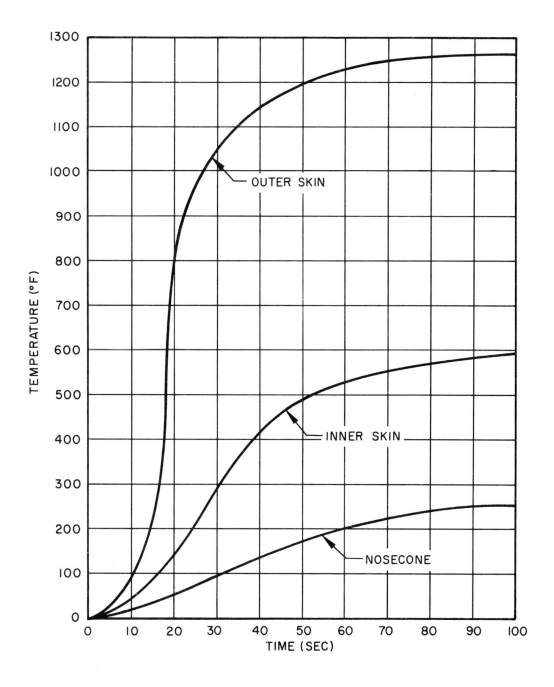

Fig. 8-2b Line Illustration: Graph With Major Grids, Leroy Callouts. This kind of illustration is used when information to be read from the graph is less specific than that shown in Fig. 8-2a but more specific than that indicated in Fig. 8-2c

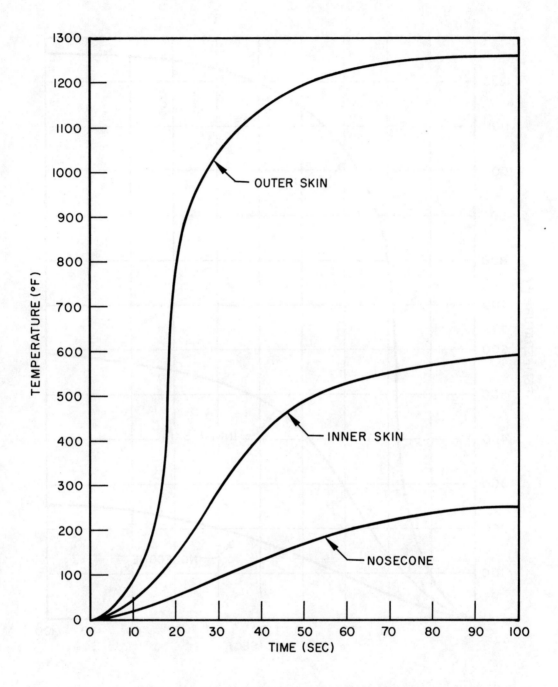

Fig. 8-2c Line Illustration: Graph With Numbers and Tick Marks on Axes, Leroy Callouts. This kind of illustration is used to show a trend or to provide information that need not be detailed and precise

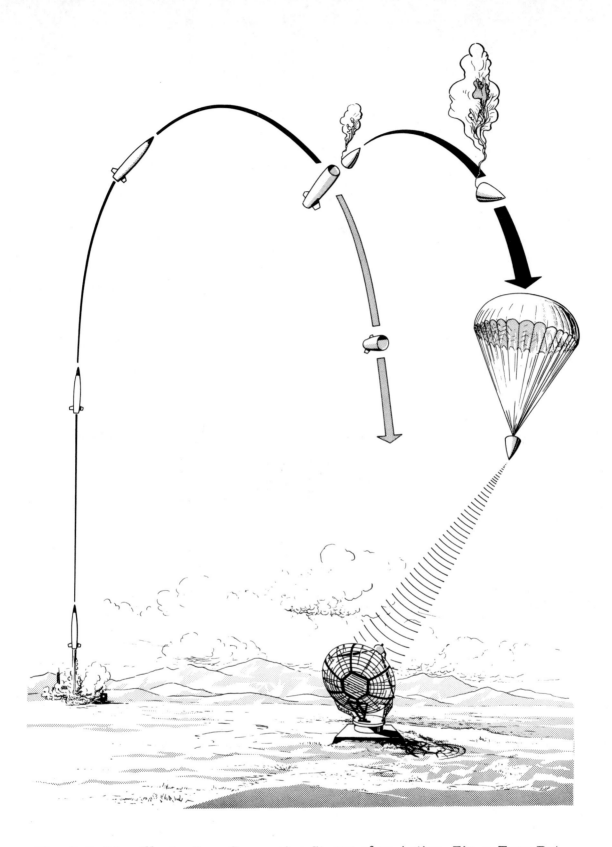

Fig. 8-3 Line Illustration: Successive Stages of an Action, Zip-a-Tone Patterns for Simulation of Halftone Effects

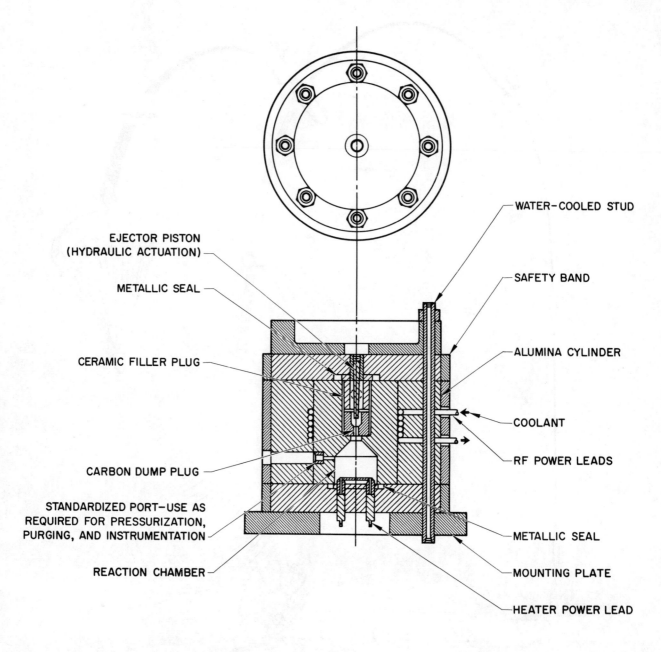

EJECTOR PISTON
(HYDRAULIC ACTUATION)

METALLIC SEAL

CERAMIC FILLER PLUG

CARBON DUMP PLUG

STANDARDIZED PORT—USE AS
REQUIRED FOR PRESSURIZATION,
PURGING, AND INSTRUMENTATION

REACTION CHAMBER

WATER-COOLED STUD

SAFETY BAND

ALUMINA CYLINDER

COOLANT

RF POWER LEADS

METALLIC SEAL

MOUNTING PLATE

HEATER POWER LEAD

Fig. 8-4 Line Illustration: Cross Section, Zip-a-Tone Patterns for Differentiation,
Leroy Callouts

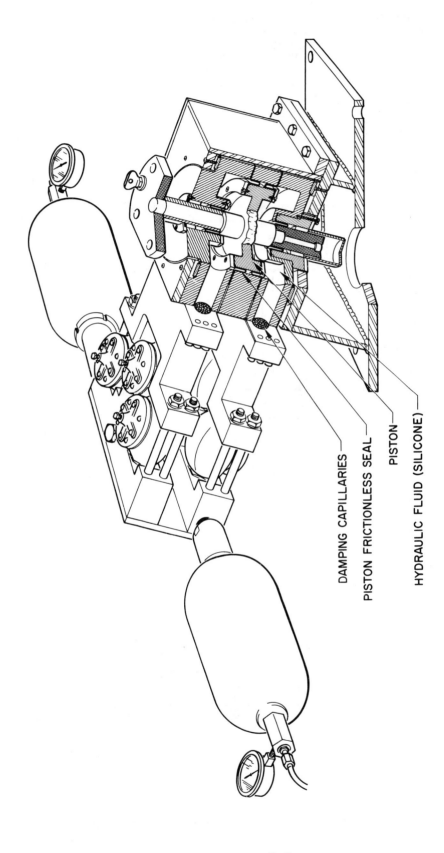

DAMPING CAPILLARIES

PISTON FRICTIONLESS SEAL

PISTON

HYDRAULIC FLUID (SILICONE)

Fig. 8-5 Line Illustration: Cutaway, Zip-a-Tone Patterns for Differentiation, Leroy Callouts

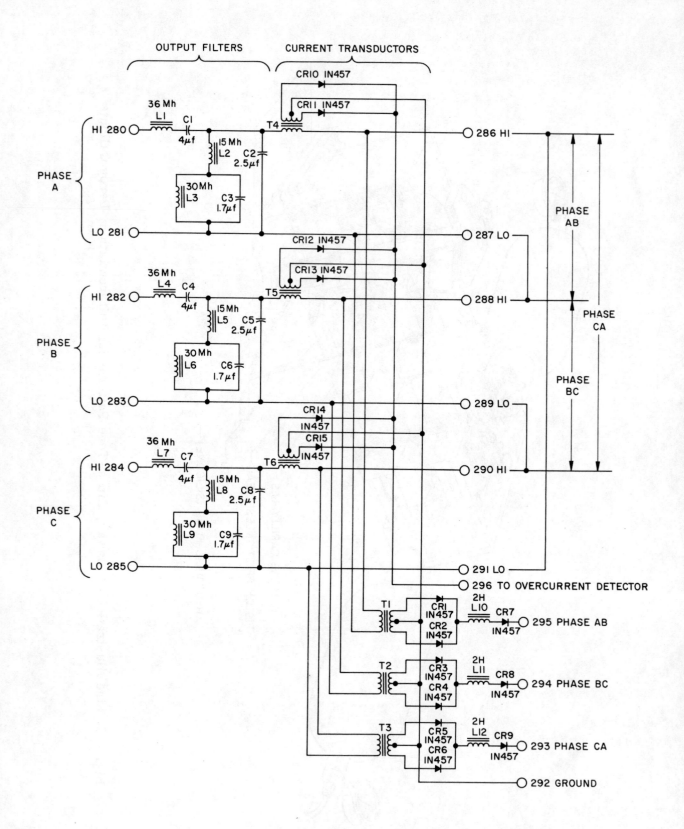

Fig. 8-6 Line Illustration: Electronic Schematic, Leroy Callouts

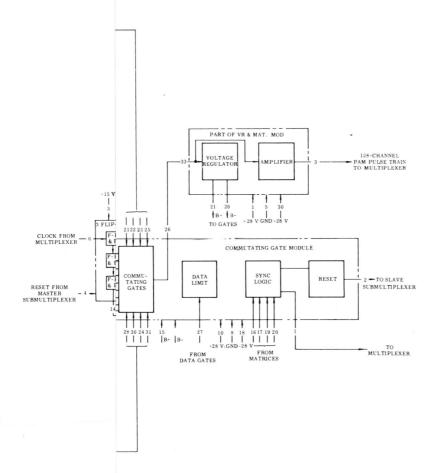

8.2.2 Halftone Illustrations

Examples of halftone illustrations are shown in Figs. 8-8a, 8-8b, and 8-9. Photographs, retouched photographs, and airbrush renderings are the most commonly used halftone illustrations.

Since contrast is often lost in reproduction, a better printing plate results from a glossy print than from a dull-finish print. To reproduce well, the print must have:

- Good lighting
- Sharp detail
- Adequate contrast
- Definite plane areas
- Uncluttered background

Figures 8-8a and 8-8b illustrate the cropping of a large print, the enlargement of specific features, and the removal of extraneous items by airbrushing. Callouts may be provided for additional clarity.

As noted in Chapter 2, if the technical writer or editor works in close collaboration with the author during preparation of a publication, he will be able to contribute to the planning and selection of photographs. He will know the specific purpose that the photographs are to serve and will be able to make pertinent suggestions to the photographer.

8.3 Handling of Artwork

8.3.1 Preparation of Copy for Art Group

The artists receiving rough material for final preparation must have certain information or instructions. Much valuable time will be saved and meeting deadlines

Fig. 8-8a Halftone Illustration: Unretouched Photograph

Fig. 8-8b Halftone Illustration: Retouched Photograph. The photograph presented in Fig. 8-8a has been cropped, blown up, and airbrushed

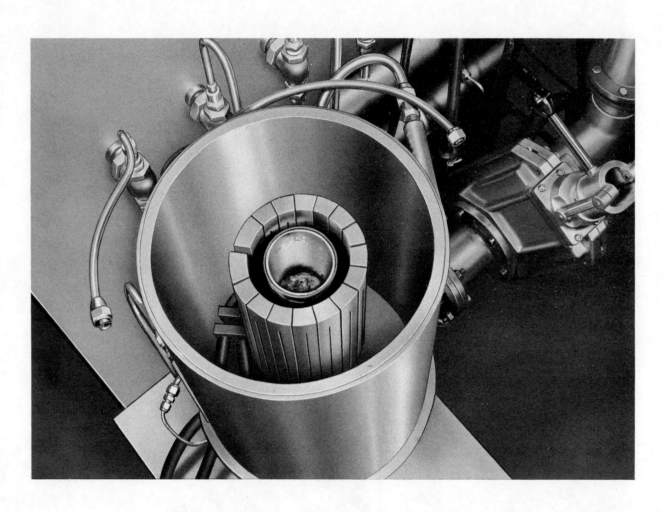

Fig. 8-9 Halftone Illustration: Airbrush Drawing

will be somewhat easier if the author, or the editor in conference with the author, makes comments or markings on the artwork itself. For each line illustration, he should:

- Indicate whether a graph is to be made on paper having many fine grids (Fig. 8-2a), on bond or vellum with major grids only (Fig. 8-2b), or on bond or vellum with numbers and tick marks only (Fig. 8-2c)
- Indicate whether a graph is to be used to provide quantitative information or merely suggest a trend
- Identify Greek symbols
- Use a colored pencil to mark subscripts and superscripts with the symbols $\wedge$ and $\vee$, respectively
- Use conventional editorial marks to indicate capital letters ($\underline{\underline{c}}$) or lowercase letters ($\not{D}$ or lc)
- Clarify the numbering and identification of axes; e.g., Altitude h (thousands of ft)
- Specify whether typewritten (Fig. 8-1) or mechanical lettering (Leroy or Wrico) is to be used for callouts and identification of axes
- Specify whether the illustration is to appear in vertical or broadside position
- Indicate whether the illustration is to appear on a page with text, on a page with other illustrations, as a full-size page, or as a foldout
- Stamp the appropriate security classification on the illustration

8.3.2 Preparation of Finished Artwork for Printing

After the artwork is completed, the artist marks it for reduction and returns it to the editor. Both size and rendering will determine whether the plates are made by xerography or photography.

When a simple line illustration (size for size) is combined with text (Fig. 8-1), the master copy of the text is prepared on bond paper (for reasons discussed on page 9-2), the illustration is taped to the paper, and a Xerox plate is made.

When xerography is used to reduce or enlarge the completed artwork, it is customary to make a Xerox bond or vellum of the illustration only. The caption, page number, and company document number are then added to the xeroxed bond or vellum and a Xerox plate is made. This procedure allows a uniform type size throughout the publication.

Halftone illustrations or line illustrations which have been prepared to simulate tone effects by the use of Zip-a-Tone or similar material (Fig. 8-3) must be reproduced photographically. For such illustrations, the negative must contain all materials that will appear on the printed page. In addition to the artwork, the editor must also submit the page number, company document number, and caption for each illustration. These are typed on bond paper which is then photographed. The resulting negative or negatives are stripped into the negative of the artwork. The image of the composite negative is transferred directly onto a sensitized metal or paper plate from which the page is printed.

8.4 Callouts in Text

For convenience, all illustrations are identified as figures and are usually printed on numbered pages. Each illustration must be called out in the text and, where possible, immediately follows the first reference to it. Since an illustration is usually presented on a separate page, the reference should be by number rather than by a phrase such as the figure below or the following illustration. Consequently, the callout usually consists of the abbreviation Fig. (or Figure if it is the first word of a sentence), followed by the figure number.

The callout may be an integral part of a sentence, or it may be given parenthetically. When the parenthetical material appears within a sentence, the introductory see is not required. (An example of recommended usage is found on page 12-6.)

When the pages of a publication are numbered in sequence by chapter, rather than consecutively throughout the publication, the illustrations are also numbered by chapter. Two Arabic numerals separated by a hyphen are used to designate a particular illustration. The first numeral identifies the chapter; the second designates the sequence of the illustration within that chapter. When an illustration consists of two or more closely related parts, each part is identified by a lowercase letter following the second Arabic numeral. Thus, Fig. 8-2b refers to the second part of the second illustration in this chapter.

8.5 Captions

A figure caption should describe the illustration clearly and concisely. If possible, it should be expressed as a noun phrase, yet it should be sufficiently descriptive to suggest the purpose or content of the illustration. The usefulness of the illustration and hence the justification for its inclusion are indicated by the caption.

The caption is typed in capital and lowercase letters and is centered about 1/2 inch (or three typewriter spaces) below the illustration. It appears on the same line with Fig. (initial capital only) and the pertinent number, with two spaces between the number and the first word. When the parts of a multiple-part illustration appear on the same page, a caption may be supplied below each; however, the caption for the entire illustration should be phrased to include all the parts. (See Fig. 9-1.)

If necessary, the caption is punctuated internally, but a period is used only to separate the first part of the caption from any additional explanatory matter. The additional matter is not terminated by a period, even when it is expressed in sentence form. Only the initial letter is capitalized when the explanation is a sentence.

When the caption requires more than one line, it is single spaced. The first word of the second line or succeeding lines is placed flush with the first word of the preceding line.

When the illustration appears in a broadside (twist) position, the caption is also placed in broadside position; but the page number and company document number are in the regular position, as though the page had not been rotated 90 degrees.

Typical captions are listed below:

Fig. 4-3 Maximum Surface Range Versus Satellite Altitude for Direct
Readout Where Equipment Range Is Varied To Permit Line-
of-Sight Operation at 150 nm

Fig. 5-2 Light Emission From the End of a Silvered Cylinder

Fig. 5-5 The Lockheed Van de Graaff Laboratory. The apparatus on
the right is a gamma-ray scintillation detector for angular-
distribution measurements

Fig. 6-1a Increase of the Lower Frequencies With Initial Pressure
for Purely Circumferential Modes

Fig. 8-13 Analog Telemetry Processing Station

Chapter 9
MATHEMATICS AND OTHER SYMBOLIC MATERIAL

9.1 Introduction

Symbols provide a concise and unique method for presenting certain concepts. Mathematical equations, chemical formulas, spectroscopic terms, and mathematical derivations are typical examples of such usage. Although mathematics is an essential part of the physical-science vocabulary, equations in a technical publication tend to reduce its readability. Ideally, the mathematical development will be made in such a way that even readers who are not skilled mathematicians will understand the principal theme. They will assume that the equations provide the necessary supporting evidence.

The readability of mathematics depends largely upon the cooperation of the author and editor in preparing the copy for reproduction. Since symbols require special characters and nonuniform lining positions, they are not easy to use when typewritten copy must be prepared. Such copy is limited by the symbols available on the typewriter and by the fact that the typists are not mathematicians. Both author and editor must be aware of these limitations. An author must write formulas and equations very carefully so that the letters and signs are clear and all expressions are in correct form. The editor must supervise the typing to make sure that the copy accurately reflects the author's intent.

Specific concerns of the author and editor in their joint effort to produce effective mathematical copy for a technical publication are considered in the material that follows.

9.2 Preparation of the Master Copy

9.2.1 Equipment and Materials

Copy which contains mathematics is typed on a special typewriter equipped with interchangeable keys. (See Fig. 9-1a.) These characters may be supplemented by Artype symbols (Fig. 9-1b) which are available in various sizes. The symbols have an adhesive backing and are easily attached to the master copy.

Heavy sulphite bond is used for copy containing equations. This type of paper is particularly satisfactory because it withstands erasures well. It is possible, for example, to erase mistakes, to paint the area containing these mistakes with Snopake, and to type the corrections over the resulting snow-white surface. When a section of bond paper requires extensive corrections, these may be made on another section which is stripped into the master or reproduction copy. If carefully made, the corrections will not be detected on the printed copy. Proofreading marks should be made in light blue, which will not be reproduced when a printing plate is made by photography or xerography. (For a description of xerography, see page 2-8.)

9.2.2 Preparation of Manuscript

Although reproduction copy may be readily corrected, the typing of mathematics is not easy, and considerable time is needed to type the material correctly. The preparation and typing of copy will be expedited if the author makes his original draft crystal-clear. For instance, to guide the editor and the typist, he should:

- Mark superscripts and subscripts at their first appearance
- Write the name of each Greek letter in the margin when it first appears

α	alpha	η	eta	ν	nu	υ , Υ	upsilon
β	beta	θ	theta	ξ , Ξ	xi	ϕ , Φ	phi
γ , Γ	gamma	ι	iota	π , Π	pi	χ	chi
δ , Δ	delta	κ	kappa	ρ	rho	ψ , Ψ	psi
ϵ	epsilon	λ , Λ	lambda	σ , Σ	sigma	ω , Ω	omega
ζ	zeta	μ	mu	τ	tau		

ℓ	script L	$\sim$	similar to; difference; asymptotically proportional	( ) $\big(\ \big)$	parentheses
$\imath$	italic L	$\approx$	approximately equals	[ ] $\big[\ \big]$	brackets
∂	partial derivative	$\cong$	congruent to		
∇	del or nabla; vector differential operator	$\rightarrow$	vector	{ } $\big\{\ \big\}$	braces
		$\rightleftarrows$	approaches limit of; yields		
∞	infinity				
∞	varies as	$\times$	multiplied by	$\int$ $\int$	integral
$>$	greater than	$+$	plus		
$<$	less than	$=$	equals	$\sqrt{\ }$ $\sqrt{\ }$	radical; root; square root
$\geq$	not less than	$\equiv$	identical with		
$\leq$	not greater than	$\circ$	degree	$\sum$	sum
		$|$	absolute value of		

a. Special Typewriter Letters and Symbols

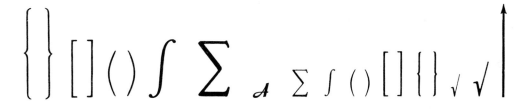

b. Typical Artype Symbols

Fig. 9-1 Letters and Symbols Available for Mathematical Copy

- Differentiate symbols that may be ambiguous (e.g., the lowercase 1, the script ℓ, and the number 1; the capital O and the zero 0; the lowercase x and the times sign ×)

- Place an arrow above each vector

$$\vec{A} \text{ and } \vec{v}, \quad \vec{A} \times \vec{B} = \vec{k} AB \sin \theta$$

- Use the sequence $\{[(\;)]\}$ for signs of aggregation, except where conventional notation specifies brackets or braces

- Make aggregation, integral, and summation signs the same height as the expressions which they include, or slightly larger

- Use the solidus instead of the horizontal bar in fractions appearing in text, or display the material containing the fractions

- Use fractional exponents instead of radical signs

- Use the abbreviation exp followed by the exponent in parentheses (instead of e raised to a power) when an exponent contains two or more quantities

$$\exp(a + bi) \quad \underline{\text{instead of}} \quad e^{a+bi}$$

- Use parentheses to enclose an argument that contains a plus or minus sign

$$\cos(\omega t - \beta x)$$

- Number only the principal, or key, equations

9.2.3 Spacing Within Equations

Spacing of each sign and symbol in equations must be meticulous if a mathematical presentation is to be correct and uniform. The following rules concern the spacing of material both within displayed equations and within text.*

---

*Spacing is expressed in units for the IBM Executive Typewriter with Bold Face No. 2 type, and in spaces for the standard typewriter.

- Place subscripts and superscripts, respectively, half a line below and above the lowest and highest characters in the related material.

$$\text{Examples:} \quad R_1 \quad , \quad 2\left(\frac{N_{\phi_1}}{Eh}\right)^{1/2}$$

- Align subscripts with superscripts.

$$\text{Examples:} \quad P_n^2 \quad , \quad F_\mu^{(p,q)}$$

- Place sub-subscripts half a line below the subscripts.

$$\text{Example:} \quad E_{x_o}$$

- Use lowercase o's for both subscript and superscript zeros, except in juxtaposition to other superscript or subscript numbers.

$$\text{Examples:} \quad K_o^2 \quad , \quad f_2(t_0) = f_2(t_1) \quad , \quad n^{0.15}$$

- Raise th to a superscript position.

$$\text{Examples:} \quad n^{th} \quad , \quad i^{th}$$

- In displayed equations, leave 3 units (1 space) before and after the operational signs $+$, $-$, $\pm$, $\times$, and $\cdot$ (a soft-rolled period) when these signs indicate that a quantity is being added to, subtracted from, added to or subtracted from, or multiplied by another quantity; for in-text equations, leave 2 units (1 space) before and after such signs.

Exception: Leave no space before and after such signs in subscripts and superscripts, except for 1 unit before and after an equals sign.

$$\text{Examples:} \quad a + b \quad , \quad \dots \text{if } a + b = 10 \text{ and the}\dots.$$

$$na^{n-1} \quad , \quad \sum_{x=o}$$

- Leave 1 unit (no space) after $+$, $-$, and $\pm$ when these indicate the sign of a single term in the text or a single term enclosed in parentheses or brackets in an equation.

  Examples: ... within ± 4 cm ....   , $P(x) = - \phi_o(-x) + R$

- Leave 4 units (2 spaces) before and after $=$, $>$, $<$, $\geq$, and $\leq$ in displayed equations, and 3 units (1 space) for in-text equations.

  Exception: Leave 1 unit (no space) before these signs in subscripts and superscripts.

  Examples: $2xy = b^2$,   ... in $2xy = b$ we find ....

$$\sum_{k \leq o}^{\infty} a_k (z - a)^k \quad , \quad |z_\alpha| < a$$

- Leave 1 unit (no space) before and after a group of three dots indicating an omission; leave no space between the dots; and type the dots on the line as if they were periods.

  Example: $\alpha = n + 1 ...$

- Align the bar of a built-up fraction with the center of the equals sign. Center the numerator and denominator relative to the horizontal bar in a built-up fraction, allowing a small space above and below the bar.

  Example: $\alpha = \dfrac{- K_a' + \sqrt{\left(K_2'\right)^2 + 4 K_a' C}}{2C}$

- Make a solidus extend from the top to the bottom of the values it separates.

  Example: $K^2 \big/ 2 C_\alpha$

- Type any required bar or dot immediately above the mathematical symbol, so that it will be obvious that the bar or dot and the symbol constitute a unit. The bar over a capital letter is made by rolling up the underscore; the bar over a lowercase letter is made by rolling up the hyphen. (For

the lowercase i , it is necessary to raise the bar or dot a little more.)
If bars are used over both capital and lowercase letters in a report, the
rolled-up underscore is used throughout.

Examples: $\bar{K}$, $\bar{k}$, $\dot{i}$, $\dot{r}$

- Leave no more than 1 unit (1 space) between the single-line elements of a
product, and leave 1 unit (no space) before punctuation within such material.
Leave 2 units (1 space) between double-line (built-up) elements of a product and 3 units (2 spaces) between elements of a product which exceeds a
double line. (See the following rule for products involving trigonometric,
logarithmic, or exponential functions.)

Examples: $2xy$, $2C$, $2C_\alpha$, $4K_a'C$, $I(M_o, N)$

$$I_o^2\left(A_o^2, N\right) \quad , \quad \frac{1}{2m}\frac{(j+m)!}{(j-m)!}$$

$$\frac{1 + \dfrac{\gamma-1}{2}M_o^2}{\eta_c}\left[\zeta_{2,3}^{(\gamma-1)/\gamma} - 1\right]$$

- Leave 2 units (1 space) before and after trigonometric, logarithmic, or exponential functions, and leave 2 units (1 space) between the parts of such
functions. If such functions must be divided, divide after an appropriate
operational sign.

Examples: $v\cos\theta$, $Y\ln x$, $2\log y\log z$, $\frac{1}{2}\exp\left(a + \frac{h}{2}\right)$

- Leave 1 unit (1 space) before and after differentials and 1 unit (1 space)
between differentials.

Examples: $x\,dx$, $(x^2 + y^2)\,dx\,dy$

- Use signs of aggregation large enough to enclose the material within. Center signs of aggregation relative to the equals sign. Leave 1 unit (no space)
between adjacent signs of aggregation.

Exception: When the material contains only simple superscripts or simple subscripts (but not both), use the standard-size typewriter keys for the signs.

Examples: $(K^2 + A)$, $\left(K^2 + A_1 + K_2 + B^2\right)$

$$Q - \left\{\left(x_a - x_b\right)^2 + \left[1 - \sin^2 \theta \, \cos\left(\pi - \theta\right)\right]\right\}$$

$$x = \begin{bmatrix} \xi_1 \\ \xi_2 \\ \cdots \\ \xi_n \end{bmatrix} = \begin{bmatrix} t_{11} \ t_{12} \cdots t_{1n} \\ t_{21} \ t_{22} \cdots t_{2n} \\ \cdots \\ t_{n1} \ t_{n2} \cdots t_{nn} \end{bmatrix} \begin{bmatrix} \bar{\xi}_1 \\ \bar{\xi}_2 \\ \cdots \\ \xi_n \end{bmatrix} = T\bar{x}$$

- Use an integral sign large enough so that it is not overshadowed by the material on either side.

Examples: $$\sqrt{\frac{a}{g}} \int_0^h \frac{dx}{\sqrt{hx - x^2}} \left(1 - \frac{x}{2a}\right)^{-1/2}$$

$$\sin^{-1} x = \int_0^x \frac{dz}{\sqrt{1 - z^2}}$$

- Center material above and below a summation sign.

Example: $$\sum_{\infty - 0}^{0}$$

- Make parallel lines long enough to extend to the top and bottom of the material between them.

Example: $\left| E^2_{x_0} \right|$

The following rules apply only to the spacing of in-text mathematical material.

- Leave 4 units (2 spaces) before and after a mathematical symbol or expression which is not treated as a word; leave 2 units (1 space) between such a symbol or expression and a punctuation mark which follows; leave 4 units (2 spaces) between a comma and whatever follows; and leave 6 units (2 spaces) between a period and the next sentence.

Examples: ... corresponding to $\bar{k}^T$, which equals ....

... the term $\bar{k}^T$.   Then the ....

- In single-spaced text, soft-roll subscripts and superscripts; type all such symbols at one time for a given line.

- If an in-text equation must be broken, break it after the equals sign or operational sign.

- Leave 4 units (2 spaces) before and after an in-text mathematical expression or an equation.

Example: ... the case $C^T = (0 \leq t \leq T)$ estimates ....

- When a mathematical expression is followed by a unit of measurement, leave 2 units (1 space) between the mathematical expression and the unit.

Example: ... the interval of $\Delta t = 0.04$ sec used in the ....

9.2.4 Display of Equations

Equations are always displayed with special indention and layout. (See Figs. 9-2 through 9-6.)

Equation (2.8) may be written more explicitly as

$$\vec{A}(q') = \int_S G(q',p)\,\vec{J}(p)\,dS - \frac{1}{k^2}\int_S \nabla'\nabla G(q',p)\cdot\vec{J}(p)\,dS$$

The integral

$$\vec{A}_1(q') = \int_S G(q',p)\,\vec{J}(p)\,dS$$

which is improper if $q' = q$, is known to converge and to define a field $\vec{A}_1$ that is continuous throughout space. This is a standard theorem in potential theory. (See Ref. 16.) On the other hand, the integral

$$\vec{A}_2(q') = \int_S \nabla'\nabla G(q',p)\cdot\vec{J}(p)\,dS \tag{2.9}$$

diverges when $q' = q$, and it is not immediately obvious what limit it approaches as $q' \to q$ (or whether it approaches a limit at all). To find the answer, we must first integrate by parts in Eq. (2.9). First, we may write

$$\vec{A}_2(q') = \nabla'\int_S \nabla G(q',p)\cdot\vec{J}(p)\,dS \tag{2.10}$$

Fig. 9-2 Display of Single-Line Equations

$$y = c_1 e^{ax} \cos ax + c_2 e^{ax} \sin ax + c_3 e^{-ax} \cos ax$$
$$+ c_4 e^{-ax} \sin ax + c_5 e^{-ax} \cos ax + c_6 e^{-ax} \sin ax$$

$$(\dot{\mu} + \dot{\nu} \tan \mu \cot \nu) \dot{\nu} = - T (mr)^{-1} \cos \mu \cos \theta \sin \epsilon$$
$$- \frac{P}{2} SV^2 C_L (mr)^{-1} \sin \phi \cos \mu$$
$$- \frac{3 g_o R^2}{2 r^2} K_\Lambda \sin 2\mu \sin 2\nu$$

$$\dot{\phi} = \omega_x + \dot{\epsilon} \sin \theta - \omega_{x_o} \cos \theta \cos \epsilon - \omega_{y_o} \cos \theta \sin \epsilon + \omega_{z_o} \sin \theta$$
$$= \omega_x + \tan \theta (\omega_4 \sin \phi + \omega_z \cos \phi) - \omega_{x_o} \cos \theta \cos \epsilon$$
$$- \omega_{y_o} \cos \theta \sin \epsilon + \omega_{z_o} \sin \theta$$

Fig. 9-3 Display of Stacked Right-Hand Member

$$\int_{-1}^{1} P_m(x) \frac{d}{dx}\left[(1 - x^2) P_n'(x) \right] dx - \int_{-1}^{1} P_n'(x) \frac{d}{dx}\left[(1 - x^2) P_m'(x) \right] dx$$

$$+ (n - m)(n + m + 1) \int_{-1}^{1} P_m(x) P_n(x) dx = 0$$

$$\left(z - z_1\right)^r \frac{d^r w}{dz^r} + \left(z - z_1\right)^r p_1(z) \frac{d^{r-1} w}{dz^{r-1}} + \left(z - z_1\right)^{r-2} p_2(z) \frac{d^{r-2} w}{dz^{r-2}}$$

$$+ \ldots + P_r(z) w = 0$$

$$\sum_n \left\{ \left[\overline{\nabla}_n^2 \overline{\nabla}_n^2 f_n + \frac{ik^2}{a} \cdot \frac{1}{2}\left(\frac{1}{a} + \frac{1}{b} \right) \overline{\nabla}_n^2 f_n \right] \cos n\theta \right.$$

$$+ \frac{ik^2}{a} \cdot \frac{1}{4}\left(\frac{1}{b} - \frac{1}{a} \right) \left[\left(\frac{d^2 f_n}{dr^2} - \frac{(2n + 1)}{r} \frac{df_n}{dr} + \frac{n(n + 2)}{r^2} f_n \right) \cos(n + 2)\theta \right.$$

$$\left. \left. + \left(\frac{d^2 f_n}{dr^2} + \frac{(2n + 1)}{r} \frac{df_n}{dr} + \frac{n(n - 2)}{r^2} f_n \right) \cos(n - 2)\theta \right] \right\} = 0$$

Fig. 9-4 Display of Stacked Left-Hand Member

$$\frac{1}{2\pi} \int_{-\infty}^{\infty} \frac{\exp(-itw_1)}{2\,\sigma_{11}\,\sigma_{12}\,\sin\theta_{12}}$$

$$\frac{dt}{\left\{ \left[\frac{1}{4}\left(\frac{1}{\sigma_{11}^2\,\sin^2\theta_{12}} - \frac{1}{\sigma_{12}^2} \right) \right]^2 + \left[\frac{1}{4}\left(\frac{1}{\sigma_{11}^2\,\sin^2\theta_{12}} + \frac{1}{\sigma_{12}^2} \right) - it \right]^2 \right\}^{1/2}}$$

$$= \frac{1}{2\pi} \int_{-\infty}^{\infty} \exp(-itw_1) \left\{ \frac{1}{2\,\sigma_{11}\,\sigma_{12}\,\sin\theta_{12}} \int_{0}^{\infty} \exp\left[-\frac{1}{4}\left(\frac{1}{\sigma_{11}^2\,\sin^2\theta_{12}} + \frac{1}{\sigma_{12}^2} \right) s \right] \right.$$

$$\left. J_0 \left[\frac{1}{4}\left(\frac{1}{\sigma_{11}^2\,\sin^2\theta_{12}} - \frac{1}{\sigma_{12}^2} \right) s \right] e^{ist}\,ds \right\} dt'$$

$$\frac{(-)^n}{n!}\, y^{2n} \left[(2 + 3 + 4 \ldots + n) + 2(3 + 4 \ldots + n) \ldots + i(i + 1 + \ldots + n) \ldots \right.$$

$$\left. + (n - 1)n \right]$$

$$= \frac{(-)^n}{n!}\, y^{2n} \left[\frac{(n - 1)(n + 2)}{2} + \frac{2(n - 2)(n + 3)}{2} \ldots + i\,\frac{(n - i)(n + i + 1)}{2} \ldots \right]$$

$$= \frac{(-)^n}{n!}\, y^{2n} \sum_{i=1}^{n} \left[(n^2 + n)\,i - i^2 - i^3 \right]$$

Fig. 9-5 Display of Stacked Right-Hand and Left-Hand Members

$$I_x \dot{\omega}_x + \dot{h}_x + \omega_y \omega_x (I_z - I_y) + \omega_y h_z - \omega_z h_y$$

$$= + \frac{3 g_o R^2}{r^3} \left(I_x \sin^2 \theta - I_y + I_z \cos^2 \theta \right) \phi \cos \theta + \frac{P}{2} u^2 Sl_x C_y + m_x$$

$$- \nabla^2 \int_{\Delta u_i} \frac{1}{3 \Sigma_a \xi \Sigma_s} q(\vec{r}) \, du + \int_{\Delta u_i} \frac{\overline{\Sigma}_a}{\xi \Sigma_s} q(\vec{r}) \, du$$

$$= - q\left(\vec{r}, u_i\right) + q(r, u_{i-i}) + P_{(\vec{r})} \int_{\Delta u_i} \chi \, du + \int_{\Delta u_i} Q(\vec{r}) \, du$$

$$- \frac{1}{3 \Sigma_{tr} \xi \Sigma_{si}} \nabla^2 \overline{q}_i(\vec{r}) + \frac{\overline{\Sigma}_u}{\xi \Sigma_s} q_i(\vec{r})$$

$$= \frac{1}{\Delta u_i} \left[- q\left(\vec{r}, u_i\right) + q\left(\vec{r}, u_{i-I}\right) \right] + P_{(\vec{r})} \chi_i + Q_i(\vec{r})$$

Fig. 9-6 Display of Equations With Both Members More Than Half a Line, but Less Than a Full Line

A single-line equation which is not part of a group of equations is centered on the line. For single-line equations which constitute a group, the longest equation is centered on the line, and the first equals sign of the other equations in the group is aligned with the first equals sign of the longest equation. If such an arrangement necessitates breaking the equations, no attempt is made to align the equals signs.

There are several possibilities for "stacking" equations that are too long for one line. The left-hand and right-hand members (to the left and right, respectively, of the first equals sign) should be presented in such a way that the reader can see at a glance where the left-hand member ends and where the right-hand member begins. Usually, the left-hand member begins flush left and the right-hand member ends flush right (unless the equation is identified by an equation number).

Usually it is possible to break an equation at an operational sign $(+, \; -, \; \pm, \; \times,$ or $\cdot$) or at an equals sign; the sign is carried over to the next line. Breaking at a sign of aggregation (parenthesis, bracket, or brace), an integral sign, or a summation sign should be carefully considered; the material preceding such a sign cannot always be separated from the sign.

An equation number, consisting of two Arabic numerals separated by a decimal, is assigned to each key equation. The numeral before the decimal point designates the particular section or chapter; the numeral after the decimal point shows the sequence of the equation within the section or chapter. When equations appear in an appendix, the letter designating the particular appendix replaces the numeral before the decimal point. The equation number is enclosed in parentheses and is typed on the last line of the equation, flush with the right-hand margin and separated from the equation by at least 1/2 inch. When an equation extends to the full length of the line, the equation number may be typed by itself on the next line flush with the right-hand margin. Equations grouped by a brace are numbered as a single equation opposite the point of the brace. When a, b, c, etc., are appended to an equation number, no space is left between the number and the letter.

The abbreviations Eq. and Eqs. (for Equation and Equations, respectively) are used with equation numbers in the text, except at the beginning of sentences. The equation number is placed in parentheses. When the abbreviation Eq. plus the equation number must be used parenthetically, the outside set of parentheses is replaced by brackets; e.g., [Eq. (4.2)].

A footnote callout should not be placed next to a mathematical symbol because the callout might be confused with an exponent.

9.3 Mathematical English

Although use of mathematics contributes to conciseness and accuracy of expression, its effective presentation depends upon good usage. Accepted practice for writing mathematics constitutes mathematical English. Some important points to be considered in discussing mathematical English concern identifying symbols in an equation, punctuating equations, and using transitional phrases.

The symbols used in a mathematical development may be identified either by special clauses after certain equations or by a list of the symbols and their identifications for all equations used in the development. The list is particularly appropriate in reports which develop a single mathematical theme. In reports containing mathematical derivations which are used only to present parts of the subject matter, clauses after equations are more suitable for identifying the symbols.

The formal listing of symbols used throughout a mathematical report is usually a part of the front matter and immediately precedes the first section of text. It is normally headed Notation. Each entry consists of a symbol and its identification. If desired, units of measurement in parentheses may be included after the identification. The symbols are aligned vertically on the left, as shown in the typical notation that follows.

NOTATION

$$E \quad mc^2$$

ν frequency

$\vec{r}$ radius vector to particle

F_x X-component of the thrust

I_o moment of inertia about axis through
the center of mass (slug-ft^2)

The words introducing the special clauses that identify the symbols in equations are placed flush with the left margin on the line below the equation, and are followed on the next line by the first symbol, an equals sign, and the identification of that symbol. The second symbol is listed on the next line, and its equals sign is aligned with the one above. Thus,

$$s = v_o t \pm \frac{1}{2} at^2$$

where

$$s \quad = \quad \text{distance}$$
$$v_o \quad = \quad \text{velocity}$$
$$t \quad = \quad \text{time}$$
$$a \quad = \quad \text{acceleration}$$

When only a few symbols must be identified, the identifications may be given without vertical alignment. In such cases, each identification is given in a subordinate clause which uses a verb if a word follows and an equals sign if a symbol follows. The first subordinating conjunction may be considered to introduce the succeeding clauses, in which the verbs may be given or understood. Each subordinate clause is punctuated as required. For example,

$$E = mc^2$$

where E is the intrinsic energy, m the mass, and c the velocity of light.

As shown in the following examples, it is permissible to use an equals sign in the principal clause, particularly if a symbol or quantity follows this sign. Where possible, however, the sign should not be used as the main verb.

| Poor | Better |
| If Eq. (1) is substituted in Eq. (8), $x = y$. | If Eq. (1) is substituted in Eq. (8), $x = y$ results. |

If Eq. (1) is substituted in Eq. (8), one finds that $x = y$.

If Eq. (1) is substituted in Eq. (8), we get $x = y$.

No commas or periods are used after displayed equations or after portions of a stacked equation. A mathematical expression introduced by such words as the term, the expression, or the symbol is not set off by commas, since it is used as a restrictive appositive. When the term or expression is named (e.g., velocity, radius, altitude) the immediately following symbol (v, r, h) is likewise considered a restrictive appositive. Thus, as illustrated in the following examples, symbols introduced or identified in the text as those to be used in an equation are not set off by commas.

The buckling displacements u , v , and w are assumed in the form of double Fourier series as shown in Eq. (4.8).

The moment M is obtained from equilibrium considerations:

$$M = 2 \int_{0}^{h/2} bx\sigma \, dy$$

The quantities β_n and α_{kn} are determined by the acoustic boundary conditions; for a shell of radius a and length L, with both of the ends closed,

$$\beta_n = \frac{an\pi}{L} \qquad \text{and} \qquad \alpha_{kn}^2 = \frac{a^2}{c^2}\omega^2 - \beta_n^2 \qquad (5.2b)$$

In a few instances, when identifications have previously been made, the symbols may be considered as nonrestrictive.

Use of we in place of one often makes a mathematical derivation appear less stilted. However, usage must be consistent throughout a derivation.

Beginning a sentence with a mathematical symbol should be avoided, since an awkward and possibly ambiguous construction will result. It is also awkward to begin a clause with a symbol when the preceding clause ends with a symbol.

Poor	Better
I_{sp} represents the specific impulse.	The term I_{sp} represents specific impulse.
If $V_x = V_y$, c is imaginary.	If $V_x = V_y$, then c is imaginary.

Dangling modifiers are not sanctioned in mathematical English. The modifier most commonly misused is the participle; it dangles when the specific word which it should logically modify has been either omitted or misplaced. To avoid this type of error, authors often refrain from using the -ing ending but succeed only in replacing the dangling participle with another type of dangling modifier. In the following examples, the corrected versions were made by:

- Supplying a word to which the dangling modifier could logically be attached

- Changing the construction to a subordinate clause

- Changing the construction to an absolute phrase

- Using the phrase as the subject and supplying the necessary verb

<u>Wrong</u>

Substituting the value of x from Eq. (1), an expression is obtained for the horizontal component of the velocity.

<u>Right</u>

Substituting the value of x from Eq. (1), we obtain an expression for the horizontal component of the velocity.

When the value of x from Eq. (1) is substituted, an expression is obtained for the horizontal component of the velocity.

<u>Wrong</u>

Having simplified both Eqs. (2.4) and (2.5), the term p_i was introduced.

<u>Right</u>

After Eqs. (2.4) and (2.5) were simplified, the term p_i was introduced.

<u>Wrong</u>

Assuming a linear correlation, a normal solution was obtained.

<u>Right</u>

Assuming a linear correlation, we obtained the following normal solution.

A linear correlation having been assumed, a normal solution was obtained.

<u>Wrong</u>

Substituting the values for $\dot{\theta}$ and $\dot{r}$ at t = 0 , the value of the amplitude is obtained.

<u>Right</u>

Substituting the values for $\dot{\theta}$ and $\dot{r}$ at t = 0 gives the value of the amplitude.

9.4 Other Symbols

Spectroscopic terms are needed in some reports. Such terms usually require a superscript before and after a capital letter as well as a subscript. These superscripts and subscripts are frequently fractional and are written with the solidus. (If available, the $\frac{1}{2}$ and $\frac{1}{4}$ typewriter keys may be used, provided that no other fractions are used in a given publication.) The degree sign is used for the odd-parity superscript.

Examples: $^{5}L_{6}^{\circ}$, $^{2}F_{3/2}^{\circ}$

Chemical symbols are common in many reports and are used for the elements whenever these appear as nouns. However, a chemical symbol is never used to begin a sentence.

A nuclide is denoted by its chemical symbol with its mass number written as a superscript; e.g., U^{235}.

The chemical formula for a compound may be used when the name of the compound is long and will occur throughout the report. On first use, the name of the compound is spelled out and is followed immediately by the formula in parentheses. Thereafter, the formula is used instead of the name. Abbreviations for long compounds may also be used.

The author must make all chemical formulas especially clear. He should differentiate between capital and lowercase letters, and should indicate when spacing and dots are needed.

Chapter 10
FOOTNOTES, REFERENCES, AND BIBLIOGRAPHY

10.1 Introduction

Footnotes, references, and bibliographies may be presented in several ways. The procedures described in this chapter are better suited to the preparation of typed copy than are methods involving the use of sequentially numbered superscripts and the extensive use of footnotes.

10.2 Footnotes

Footnotes are used primarily for explanatory material that would interfere with the continuity of the text (page 2-8) and for reference to private communications such as letters and memoranda. They may also be used for bibliographic references when only a few publications are cited.

Footnotes are designated by asterisks or other symbols rather than by superscript Arabic numerals. A satisfactory system is to designate the first footnote on a page by one asterisk, the second by two asterisks, and so forth. A new sequence is begun on each page that requires footnotes. The asterisk should follow all marks of punctuation except the dash and a closing parenthesis (if reference is made to the parenthetical material).

The number of footnotes required on a page will determine the amount of text presented on that page. Footnotes are separated from the text by a 1-inch line. In this Guide, 2 spaces are left between the last line of text and the 1-inch line; and

1-1/2 spaces are left between the line and the first footnote. Footnotes are single-spaced. The asterisks are aligned to the right and are not separated from the first words of the footnotes. (See samples in Fig. 10-1.)

10.3 References and Bibliography

10.3.1 Citation and Sequence

References cited in the text of a publication are designated by the word Reference or by the abbreviation Ref., and are numbered in the order in which they occur. (When only a few references are cited, they may be presented as footnotes.) Reference(s) is spelled out if it is the first word of a sentence; otherwise, it is abbreviated and the citation is usually enclosed in parentheses. (An introductory see is not required if the parenthetical material is contained within a sentence.) Specific page numbers, if any, are also included in the text reference (Fig. 10-1). When a reference is repeated in the text, it is cited by the number originally assigned to it. When more than one reference is cited at a time, Refs. is used and the numbers are separated by commas.

References are usually presented as the last chapter of a publication. For publications which are very long or must meet a tight deadline, references may be presented as the last subdivision of each chapter. The following titles are used: (1) References, when all of the source material has been cited in the text; (2) Cited References and Uncited References, when two lists, based on callouts or the absence of callouts in the text, are presented; and (3) Bibliography when no references have been cited in the text. Cited references are listed and numbered in the order of their citation. Uncited references are listed alphabetically by author.

The sequence of the parts of a bibliographic reference is as follows:

- Author, editor, or corporate author

  The name of an author or editor is not inverted unless given in a bibliography. (As shown in Appendix B, if a publication has more

As reported in Ref. 3, homogeneous nucleation may be promoted by special processes such as elastic vibratory techniques. The Atomic Energy Commission recently sponsored a program to study the use of elastic vibratory techniques in the preparation of beryllium.* Under this program, a literature search was made, a special furnace was designed and tested,** and various materials were investigated for use in both containers and couplers. Difficulties were encountered in finding materials which were resistant to dispersion into the beryllium under conditions of elastic vibration.

Rostoker and Berger of the Armour Research Foundation have studied the effects of vibration during solidification of nonferrous castings. In any one alloy system, a pronounced grain refinement was found at low alloy content and at low cooling rates; ultrasonic frequencies were not found necessary for achieving effective results (Ref. 4, pp. 10-15 to 10-22).

A preliminary report on grain refinement by the addition of alloys has also been published by the Massachusetts Institute of Technology. (For an abstract of this report, see Ref. 5.)

---

*Reported by John S. Whitney in a private communication dated 4 Jun 1960.
**The details of the design of this furnace will be released in a forthcoming publication.

Fig. 10-1 Examples of Footnotes and Reference Callouts

than one author or editor, only the name of the first author is inverted.) The abbreviation _ed._, set off by commas, is placed after the name of the editor; the abbreviation _eds._ is used when more than one editor is cited. A corporate author (a company, university, agency, or other organization) is entered as the first element of a bibliographic reference, even when the individual author is known. For a corporate author consisting of more than one element, the sequence is from the whole (e.g., university) to the part (e.g., laboratory). When the same author is the first entry for two or more successive references, the name is replaced by a 1-inch line (5 hyphens) in the second and subsequent references.

- Title

  The title of a bound document (e.g., a book or a periodical) is underscored. (Titles of periodicals may be abbreviated.) The title of a printed company publication and the name of a newspaper are also underscored. The title of an unpublished work, however, is enclosed in quotation marks. The title of a section or chapter of a bound document, an article in a newspaper, an abstract, or a patent is also enclosed in quotation marks.

- Individual author (if identified) of a company or agency publication

  The name of the author, preceded by the word _by_, is placed after the title.

- Edition (if other than the first)

  An Arabic numeral, followed by the ordinal suffix, is used to indicate the edition: _2nd_ (not _2d_), _3rd_ (not _3d_).

- Company document number (if any)

- Contract number (if any)

- Volume and number (if any)

  Volume is designated by the abbreviation Vol. (not Vol. No.). Number — a subdivision of a volume — is designated by No.

- Place of publication

  If the place of publication is a large or well-known city, the state is not mentioned. However, if the place of publication might be associated with more than one state, the abbreviation for the state is given.

- Publisher (if not stated as the corporate author)

  The names of well-known publishing houses may be abbreviated. For example, McGraw-Hill is adequate for McGraw-Hill Book Company, Inc.

- Date of publication

  The date of publication is often expressed in military style, particularly when the document containing the list of references is prepared for the Armed Forces. Names of months are abbreviated by three letters without periods; and the day of the month, if given, precedes the name of the month, e.g., 3 Dec 1945.

- Pages

  The inclusive page numbers are given for a section of a publication (e.g., a chapter in a book or an article in a periodical). In a bibliography, the total pages are given for all books and reports (Appendix B). The abbreviations p. and pp. are used for page and pages, respectively.

- Classification

  The classification is given for publications produced by corporate authors. Classifications are cited parenthetically and in abbreviated form: U for Unclassified; C for Confidential; S for Secret; CRD for Confidential, Restricted Data; and SRD for Secret, Restricted Data.

- Supplementary information

  The final elements in a bibliographic entry may include such information as the nature and status of unpublished material, meetings at which papers were presented, and explanations regarding translations. Such additional information is placed in parentheses.

Commas are used to separate most of the elements of a bibliographic reference; the following examples illustrate the few instances in which parentheses are used. No terminal punctuation is required.

10.3.2 Examples of References

BOOK

Harry G. Armstrong, ed., <u>Aero-Space Medicine</u>, Baltimore, Williams & Wilkins, 1961

CHAPTER IN BOOK

Sir James Jeans, "Life on Other Worlds," <u>A Treasury of Science</u>, H. Shapley, ed., New York, Harper, 1954

ARTICLE IN PERIODICAL

J. D. Chalupnik, E. Rule, and F. J. Suellentrop, "Pressure Response of Condenser Microphones at Low Ambient Pressures," <u>J. Acoust. Soc. Am.</u>, Vol. 33, Feb 1961, pp. 177−178

COMPANY OR AGENCY PUBLICATION

California Institute of Technology, Jet Propulsion Laboratory, <u>A Liquid Helium Cooled Coaxial Termination</u>, by C. T. Stelzried, CIT/JPL TR 34-224, Pasadena, Calif., 25 Jan 1961 (U)

Lockheed Missiles and Space Division, <u>AICBM-INSATRAC System Study, Semiannual Report: July−December 1959</u>, Vol. II, "Appendixes," ARDC TR 59-8, LMSD-288117, Contract AF 18(600)-1847, Sunnyvale, Calif., 22 Jan 1960 (U)

PAPER, MANUSCRIPT, OR UNPUBLISHED DOCUMENT

Larry S. Klivan and W. E. Peterson, "Application of Advanced Techniques and Automatic Equipment in the Maintenance of Surveillance Drone Systems" (paper presented at U. S. Signal Corps Maintenance Symposium, Fort Monmouth, N. J., Apr 1959)

David B. Beard, "Meteoritic Impact," <u>ARS J.</u> (in press)

Lockheed Missiles and Space Division, "Influence Coefficients for Spherical Shells," by B. R. Baker and G. B. Cline, LMSD-480817, Sunnyvale, Calif. (U) (in preparation)

ABSTRACT

R. G. Johnson, L. F. Chase, Jr., and F. J. Vaughn, "The $C^{13}(He^3, n)O^{15}$ Reaction," <u>Bull. Am. Phys. Soc.</u>, Ser. II, Vol. 6, No. 3, 24 Apr 1961, p. 236 (abstract of paper presented at 1961 Spring Meeting of American Physical Society, Washington, D. C., 24−27 Apr 1961)

PATENT   G. R. Larse (to Lockheed Aircraft Corporation), "Ratio Computer Having an Unbalancing Circuit in the Feedback Loop," U.S. Patent 2,905,385, 22 Sep 1959

ARTICLE IN
NEWSPAPER   "Red Chinese Space Projects Going Forward," Los Angeles Times, 4 Nov 1958, Pt. 1, p. 11

PART 4

ACCEPTED USAGE

Chapter 11
SENTENCE STRUCTURE and PARAGRAPHING

11.1 Introduction

This chapter briefly summarizes the basic concepts of sentence structure and paragraphing. It is not meant to be exhaustive; annotated references are provided in Appendix B for those who wish to consult standard texts in English grammar and composition.

Where appropriate, examples are given with the brief summarizing statements. Each example consists of at least two versions. One has been labeled Original Version if it does not contain gross errors and would be considered passable by very liberal grammarians. In such instances, an Improved Version has been provided. In other instances, an example has been labeled Wrong when all stylists are agreed on a violation of accepted usage. A Right version has therefore been supplied.

A statement and the example given with it may emphasize one aspect of sentence structure. However, strict categorization is not possible, for effective writing generally incorporates several aspects simultaneously. It rarely reflects only one aspect. Thus, a sentence that is well subordinated may also be an example of variety and economy. A paragraph developed by description may also be an example of development by emphasis and definition.

11.2 Sentence Structure

● Subordinate ideas are expressed in subordinate clauses.

<table>
<tr><td>Original Version</td><td>Improved Version</td></tr>
<tr><td>Except for a possible effect comparable to aerodynamic drag, the effect of the impact of the micrometeorites on the structure will be negligible. This has been shown in the works by D. Bershader and others.</td><td>As D. Bershader and others have shown, the effect of the impact of the micrometeorites on the structure will be negligible, except for a possible effect comparable to aerodynamic drag.</td></tr>
</table>

● Subordinate ideas are expressed in phrases.

<table>
<tr><td>Original Version</td><td>Improved Version</td></tr>
<tr><td>The delivery test vehicle is to be launched from the U.S.S. Robert E. Lee. The test is to be conducted at a yet undesignated site in Half Moon Bay.</td><td>The delivery test vehicle is to be launched from the U.S.S. Robert E. Lee, at a yet undesignated site in Half Moon Bay.</td></tr>
</table>

● Parallel ideas are expressed in parallel or coordinate elements of construction.

<table>
<tr><td>Original Version</td><td>Improved Version</td></tr>
<tr><td>This relationship is accomplished in three steps: first, by relating the curvature rate to the strain rate of the cylindrical sheet elements; second, the strain rate is related to stress and stress resultants through the creep law; and finally, the relationship of the stress resultants to the imposed loading is established through the equations of equilibrium.</td><td>This relationship is accomplished in three steps: first, by relating the curvature rate to the strain rate of the cylindrical sheet elements; second, by relating the strain rate to stress and stress resultants through the creep law; and finally, by relating the stress resultants to the imposed loading through the equations of equilibrium.</td></tr>
</table>

Original Version	Improved Version
Auxiliary systems will be studied to prevent damage from loosened or cracked portions of the structures and to avoid explosions. The systems will also be investigated to protect personnel.	Auxiliary systems will be studied to prevent damage from loosened or cracked portions of the structures, to avoid explosions, and to protect personnel.

- Coherence requires that all pronouns refer to specific antecedents in the sentence or in the preceding sentence.

Wrong	Right
The extreme temperatures encountered by an orbiting vehicle may contribute to creep deformations of the elements of the antenna structure. This is particularly characteristic of structural elements made of plastics or similar materials.	The extreme temperatures encountered by an orbiting vehicle may contribute to creep deformations of the elements of the antenna structure. Such deformations are particularly characteristic of structural elements made of plastics or similar materials.

Wrong	Right
A complete array of ground handling equipment has been designed, developed, and proved in continued use during the past three years, which qualifies the company for consideration as a prime contractor in the proposed program.	A complete array of ground handling equipment has been designed, developed, and proved in continued use during the past three years. This experience qualifies the company for consideration as a prime contractor in the proposed program.

Wrong	Right
Cavity backing may not be necessary in most cases, which will eliminate this as a bandwidth limiting factor.	In most cases, cavity backing may not be necessary and hence may be eliminated as a bandwidth limiting factor.

● In a coherent sentence, the verb and substantive agree, and the modifier is placed as close as possible to the item which it modifies.

Wrong	Right
This data indicates that a 325-lb payload can be delivered at 5500 nm.	These data indicate that a 325-lb payload can be delivered at 5500 nm.

Original Version	Improved Version
The two differential e q u a t i o n s have been used to simplify the displacement functions, expressing equilibrium in the plane of the shell.	The two differential e q u a t i o n s, expressing e q u i l i b r i u m in the plane of the shell, have been used to simplify the displacement functions.

Wrong	Right
Solid State Electronics is currently equipped only to perform advanced research in the fields of ferrites, semiconductors, and other solid-state materials.	Solid State Electronics is currently equipped to perform advanced research only in the fields of ferrites, semiconductors, and other solid-state materials.

Wrong	Right
Due to residual stresses, this expression is used to develop a criterion for spontaneous cracking.	This expression is used to develop a criterion for spontaneous cracking due to residual stresses.

● Coherence is achieved when a verbal phrase (1) correctly refers to the noun or pronoun that it logically modifies, or (2) is changed to a dependent clause.

Wrong	Right
Together with handling and checkout equipment, t h e transport-erection trailer will carry the test vehicle.	The transport-erection trailer will carry the test vehicle together with handling and checkout equipment.

Wrong	Right
After locating the missile on the launch rail, the umbilical is attached to the power source and to the missile.	After the missile has been located on the launch rail, the umbilical is attached to the power source and to the missile.

● An idea or ideas expressed in one long sentence may often be made more effective if expressed in two or more sentences.

Original Version	Improved Version
The best available estimates on performance capabilities and tolerances of the individual elements were obtained and then analyzed to determine their quantitative effect on position error and image smear.	The best available estimates on performance capabilities and tolerances of the individual elements were obtained. These estimates were then analyzed to determine their quantitative effect on position error and image smear.

● Choppy sentences that are apparently unrelated can be combined into one effective sentence.

Original Version	Improved Version
Research is to be directed toward any conceivable electronic systems. The electronic systems will include radar and reconnaissance apparatus. Research will also be directed toward electronic systems having applicable types of antennas.	Research is to be directed toward any conceivable electronic systems, including radar, reconnaissance apparatus, and applicable types of antennas.

● An idea is emphasized by placing key words or phrases at the end of a sentence or at the beginning.

Original Version

Of great importance is the effect of fully unfolded antenna structures on the dynamic characteristics of the vehicle as a whole.

Improved Version

The effect of the fully unfolded antenna structures on the dynamic characteristics of the vehicle as a whole is very important.

Original Version

For example, we might stiffen by internal pressure, centrifugal force, or electrostatic repulsion, all of which are essentially massless methods of stiffening.

Improved Version

Essentially massless methods of stiffening might be used, such as internal pressure, centrifugal force, or electrostatic repulsion.

● Emphasis is often achieved by the use of verbs rather than nouns formed from them, and by the use of verbs in the active rather than the passive voice.

Original Version

Drainage of the area is accomplished by three streams.

Improved Versions

The area is drained by three streams.

Three streams drain the area.

Original Version

Telemetering of the data from the artificial satellite is done by a PAM-FM system on a frequency of 10.2 Mc.

Improved Versions

Data are telemetered from the artificial satellite by a PAM-FM system on a frequency of 10.2 Mc.

The PAM-FM system telemeters data from the artificial satellite on a frequency of 10.2 Mc.

● Variety is achieved by varying the lengths of sentences and the position of modifiers.

Original Version	Improved Version
Drone reconnaissance systems for land- and sea-launch positions should be developed. To ensure the proper evaluation of the necessary reconnaissance data in an environment which may make the operation of manned aircraft difficult, a land- and sea-based drone system consisting of vehicles plus data-processing equipment is required.	Land- and sea-based drone reconnaissance systems should be developed. These systems, consisting of data-processing equipment, would ensure proper evaluation of the necessary data in an environment which may make operation of manned aircraft difficult.

● An economical sentence avoids needlessly long or complicated constructions.

Original Version	Improved Version
In designing delivery systems for offensive use, in the Committee's opinion, the basic prerequisite of these is the delivery accuracy of these systems.	High-accuracy delivery systems will be required for offensive use.

● An economical sentence avoids hackneyed or roundabout expressions.

Hackneyed	Preferred
make an adjustment in	adjust
due to the fact that	because
owing to the fact that	because, since
despite the fact that	although
on the basis of	based on, by, from
in recognition of this fact	therefore
in large measure	largely
give consideration to	consider
prior to	before
subsequent to	after
throughout the entire	throughout
referring to Fig. 4 it will be noted that	Fig. 4 shows
leaving out of consideration	disregarding
the greatest percent	most
is such as to negate the feasibility of	precludes
is essential that	must
it appears that	apparently
circular in shape	circular
to make an approximation as to how much	to estimate, to approximate

11.3 Effective Paragraphing

● An effective paragraph will:

Develop a clear-cut stage of the topic

Show a clear relationship of the sections or subsections to the subject

Contain closely related sentences that fully develop one thought

Convey an idea that is closely related to the idea of the preceding paragraph

- A paragraph is generally opened with a topic sentence that states the main idea to be developed.

- Transitions within and between paragraphs are achieved by the use of pronouns, conjunctive adverbs (however, therefore, nevertheless), and conjunctive adverbial phrases (for this reason, in fact, for example, in contrast, on the other hand).

- A topic sentence is developed into an effective paragraph by description.

The Manual Data Input Unit is a component of the automatic telemetering calibration system. It may be remotely located from the Function Control Panel to which is it connected. The unit records five columns of information. It consists of rotary switches for indenting digits 0 through 9, and a toggle switch for indicating negative values. (An X-punch in the units column is used to indicate a minus value.) By this means, the Manual Data Input is used to record any data which are not automatically measured and punched. Appearance of each selected digit in a window of the unit eliminates any ambiguity due to parallax. When a Punch Ready Lamp on the panel receives its power from the Summary Punch, the unit has cards at the punching station.

- A topic sentence is developed into an effective paragraph by argumentation (through cause and effect, reasons, or both).

A similar discrepancy exists in electric quadrupole moments. The moments observed for nuclei far from the closed shells are many times too large to be accounted for by the charge asymmetry that could be produced by the single odd proton. Furthermore, odd neutron nuclei are observed to have appreciable electric quadrupole moments, although no charge asymmetry can be expected from the neutrons themselves. These multi-pole moments are related to the large gamma-ray transition rates which are often observed and which must be regarded as anomalous when the independent particle model is considered.

- A topic sentence is developed into an effective paragraph by <u>enumeration</u>.

A three-phase study will be undertaken in the proposed investigation of metal-water reactions. The first phase will make a theoretical and experimental evaluation of reaction thermodynamics and kinetics. The second phase will be concerned with the development of inhibitors for the reactions. The final phase will make use of the experimental data in the reevaluation of reactor hazards.

- A topic sentence is developed into an effective paragraph by <u>comparison and contrast</u>.

The (d, n) reactions are expected to take place by two general modes: (1) formation of a highly excited compound nucleus which results when the deuteron combines with the target and which subsequently decays by neutron or proton emission; and (2) stripping. Reactions which take place through a compound-nucleus state should show angular distributions which are nearly symmetric about 90 degrees. The yield as a function of incident deuteron energy should exhibit resonances corresponding to excited states in the compound nucleus; and when several energy groups of particles are emitted, the group with highest energy and therefore greatest statistical weight should tend to be the most intense. In stripping events, on the other hand, the annular distributions are peaked in the forward direction, the yields are not sensitive to the excited states in the target-nucleus-plus-deuteron system, and the groups of emitted particles with velocities approximately equal to that of the incident deuteron are favored. Analysis of the experimental data can thus be expected to shed light on the relative probabilities of the two mechanisms.

- A topic sentence is developed into an effective paragraph by <u>details in sequence</u>.

Stage III, priority control, is next in sequence. Should there be an urgent request for a certain report, the document will be temporarily sidetracked for immediate transmittal to an analyst. The document is then considered for copying at Stage IV, and, if possible, a copy is made at Stage V. The copy is sent immediately to the requestor, and the original is returned to the normal channels for processing. If the document cannot be copied, the original is sent to the requestor directly, and Priority Control is so notified. Priority Control has the ultimate responsibility of returning the document to the system for further processing.

- A topic sentence is developed into an effective paragraph by <u>definition</u>.

Fundamental tangential modes of a gas and shell may now be defined. They are the modes of oscillation which are independent of the axial coordinate X and thus correspond to the modes of an infinitely long shell. When such correspondence occurs, the acoustic, mechanical, and geometric boundary conditions at the ends of the shell need not be considered.

- A topic sentence is developed into an effective paragraph by <u>example</u>.

These extractors may be used to define the numerical limits of a search. For example, if data were desired on some particular item in the area within 1° of latitude and 1° of longitude of Moscow, it would be necessary to specify two pairs of descriptors. One pair might be the latitude of Moscow plus 1° and the latitude of Moscow minus 1°; the other pair, the equivalent longitude functions. For such a system, all coordinate data need not be in latitude and longitude; only standard notation must be used. Other items which may be similarly marked and located are dates and weapon capabilities.

Chapter 12
PUNCTUATION and OTHER CONVENTIONS of WRITING

12.1 Introduction

This chapter treats the marks of punctuation and related conventions most commonly encountered in technical writing. Statements on underscoring and the non-use of periods are instances of one acceptable format, as illustrated throughout this Guide. When grammarians are not in full agreement on the specific use of a certain mark of punctuation, a choice is made in the interest of uniformity. Detailed discussions are presented in the standard texts listed in the annotated bibliography (Appendix B).

12.2 Comma

A comma is used:

- After an introductory adverbial clause

  Because the emitted particle tends to retain the velocity vector of the deuteron, the characteristic feature of the stripping process is a forward peaking of the angular distributions of emitter particles.

- After an introductory phrase

  At this point, an identification number is attached to the document.

  To avoid the problem of materials, several novel geometries were used.

  In talking about a particular descriptor or extractor, we shall use the symbols d_n for the nth bit of a descriptor and e_n for the nth bit of the extractor being compared.

- Before the conjunction preceding the last item in a series

  Various types of neutron, charged-particle, or gamma-ray detectors are available.

  The work schedule provided for preliminary experiments, on-site checkouts, and arming and fuzing tests.

  NOTE: In the second example, the last item in the series is a compound unit and hence is not broken by a comma.

- Before and after nonrestrictive or interrupting elements

  The velocity error, which resulted from gravitational anomalies, is assumed to be the same after five revolutions.

  This system, consisting of a six-channel FM/FM telemeter, obtains highly accurate information under the severe environmental conditions encountered by a hypersonic, ballistic test vehicle.

- After conjunctive adverbs and adverbial phrases (however, nevertheless, furthermore, therefore, namely, hence, accordingly, that is, for example)

  Accordingly, it was decided to investigate the possibilities of a regressive thrust program.

  This curve is dependent on the size, i.e., the mass ratio, of the upper stages.

- Before the coordinating conjunction that joins two independent clauses

  These targets will be bombarded with 3-Mev protons from the Van de Graaff accelerator, and the resulting gamma radiation will be observed with a scintillation coincidence spectrometer.

- With numbers of four or more digits (Chapter 14)

- Between elements of a bibliographical entry (Chapter 10)

A comma is <u>not</u> used in a date:

- When only the month and year are given

    March 1958

- When military style is used

    21 March 1958

12.3 Semicolon

A semicolon is used:

- Between two independent clauses that are not joined by a coordinating conjunction

    The missileborne television package is extremely versatile and compact; its volume is less than 200 cu in., and its weight is less than 15 lb.

    The unit is completely transistorized; silicon transistors and diodes are used to ensure reliable operation at high temperature.

- Before a conjunctive adverb that stands between two independent clauses

    An automatic plotter operating from an IBM card reader was developed and has been in operation for some time; however, an automatic plotter is being constructed to operate directly from the magnetic-tape output of the IBM 704 computer.

    The relative station location in an earth-centered inertial system is strongly influenced by the rotation of the earth; however, the rate of rotation is nearly constant, and variations are generally predictable.

- Before a coordinating conjunction that joins two independent clauses when one or both contain internal punctuation

- The entire field of possibilities for nuclear light sources has been surveyed; and, at present, radioactively powered incandescent spheres, radioactive fluors, and electron-irradiated fluors appear to be the only promising approaches to nuclear methods of battle-field illumination.

12.4 Colon

A colon is used:

- After a word or phrase that introduces a formal listing

- Before a sentence that is a restatement or an equivalent of an immediately preceding statement

  Only the elements that do not involve the acceleration are used: The last column and the last row are neglected.

12.5 Period

A period is <u>not</u> used:

- After titles or headings

- After a caption (Chapter 8)

- After each item of a formal listing introduced by a sentence, preceded by a colon, and consisting only of words, phrases, or dependent clauses

- After abbreviations for units of measurement (except in the case of <u>in.</u>, to avoid confusion with the preposition)

- After table or figure numbers

12.6 Quotation Marks

Quotation marks are used:

- For cited titles of articles, chapters, unpublished material, and patents (Chapter 10)

- After a comma that interrupts or terminates a quotation (before the sentence is completed)

- "Airplanes," Vice President Carl B. Squier commented, "can't be bought off the shelf like a can of sardines."

- After a period, question mark, or exclamation point that terminates a quotation

- Before a colon, semicolon, question mark, or dash that is not a part of the quotation

  It is now possible to consider "purely longitudinal modes"; these are defined as those modes of oscillation of the gas-shell system which are independent of the coordinate and are thus axisymmetrical with respect to the axis of the shell.

12.7 Underscoring

To indicate italics in typed copy, underscoring is used:

- To identify names and titles of publications (Chapter 10)

  NOTE: All words and any internal punctuation are underscored with a continuous line.

- To set off run-in sideheads

- To indicate names of ships and airplanes

  U. S. S. Norton Sound

  the Jetstream, a Model 1649A Starliner

- To refer to words and expressions simply as words, or to identify matter following the terms entitled, the word, the term, and the expression

    The word velocity is not a synonym for speed.

    We call this 20-bit word the excerpt.

- To emphasize words or statements

    In the English language, there is a class of common words which are important to the communication of a thought but which have little or no value in the description of what is being said.

12.8 Parentheses

Parentheses are used:

- To enclose identifying equation numbers

- To enclose a callout to a figure, table, or reference when the callout is not an integral part of the sentence

    The scattered coronal light in this effect was measured by Blackwell at different elongations and for different wavelengths. (See Ref. 11.)

    The scattered coronal light in this effect was measured by Blackwell (Ref. 11) at different elongations and for different wavelengths.

    NOTE: When the callout appears parenthetically within a sentence, the introductory see is not required.

- To enclose numbers that precede the items of a listing

12.9 Capitals

Full capitals are used for:

- Section or chapter titles

- First-order sideheads

- Titles of tables

- Callouts on illustrations

- Identification of axes on graphs

- Abbreviated forms of proper names

AFMDC	IGY
AICBM	IRBM
NASA	IRE

Capitals and lowercase letters are used for:

- Figure captions

- Second-order sideheads

- Column headings of tables

NOTE: Unless they begin a heading or caption, the following are not capitalized: articles (a, an, the); prepositions of three letters or less (at, by, for, of, on); and conjunctions of three letters or less (and, as, but, if, or, nor).

Initial capitals are used for:

- The words table, figure, appendix, section, and chapter when followed by a number or letter

- The first word in a run-in sidehead

- The first word in each item of a column listing

- The first word of a sentence that follows a colon

- Trade names

Amphenol	Ozalid
Fiberglas	Plexiglas
Inductrol	Teflon
Monel	Vidicon
Multilith	Xerox

- A proper name specifying an item, effect, or phenomenon

Bessel function	Helmholtz coil
Boltzmann's constant	Hertz antenna
Faraday rotation	Laplace transform
Fourier series	Reynolds number

NOTE: Usage sanctions the lowercasing of some proper names.

bunsen burner	macadam road
diesel engine	pitot tube
gaussian distribution	venturi meter

12.10 Hyphen

A hyphen is used between:

- Words forming a unit modifier and between abbreviations and words forming a unit modifier of an immediately following noun

  NOTE: When a unit modifier includes compound words that have a common base, hyphens are placed after all elements dependent on that base.

  ceria-thoria coating

  gas-shell system

  land- and sea-based operations

  DC- and AC-generating equipment

  metal-water reaction

  rate-controlling step

  third- or fourth-order sideheads

  time-of-flight spectrometer

  time-to-pulse-height analyzer

  22-acre site

  UHF-radiating antenna

  PPI-scope image

NOTE: Distinction should be made between words used as a unit modifier of an immediately following noun and those used as independent modifiers. Incorrect use of the hyphen may result in a distortion of meaning, as illustrated below.

Example	Meaning
direct-current flow	flow of direct current
direct current flow	current flow that is direct
low-velocity measurements	measurements of low velocities
low velocity measurements	velocity measurements that are low
high-temperature readings	readings of high temperatures
high temperature readings	temperature readings that are high
variable-phase relationships	relationships of variable phases
variable phase relationships	phase relationships that are variable

- Two or more words forming a single item, concept, or compound unit

angle-of-attack	lb-sec
ft-lb	rate-of-climb
candle-power	state-of-the-art

- Duplicated prefixes that are normally joined to words

	Exception
sub-subheading	micromicrofarad
super-superscript	

- A prefix or suffix joined to a capitalized word

mid-August	pre-Polaris
pre-IGY	Florida-like

- A prefix and a verb that might otherwise be confused with another verb of different meaning

Example	Meaning
re-sort	sort again
re-collect	collect again

- A prefix ending in _i_ and a word beginning with _i_

    anti-icing

    semi-impermeable

A hyphen is _not_ used:

- Between an adverb ending in _-ly_ and a present or past participle

    carefully defined parameters   poorly conducted experiments

    highly polished crystal   rapidly decaying nuclide

- Between dates, page numbers, and proper nouns used as a compound (page 12-12)

- After certain prefixes (_bi_, _co_, _ex_, _in_, _inter_, _mid_, _non_, _over_, _pre_, _pro_, _re_, _sub_, _super_, _un_, _under_) unless followed by a proper noun or proper adjective

cooperation	redo
coordinates	retest
nonlinear	subindex
overrate	subboreal
overrun	supersonic

- Before suffixes or words used as suffixes unless the combination would result in tripling a consonant

cutoff	massless
feedback	shell-like
inertialess	turretlike
lengthwise	twofold

12.11 Dash

A dash is made on the typewriter by an underscore raised half a space.*

A dash is used:

- To introduce a final summarizing clause in a sentence which contains several elements as subject of the main clause

  The piston-engine F-51 Mustangs, Lockheed Shooting Stars, F-84 Thunderjets — these were the airplanes that the United Nations first used in Korea against the Russian-built MIG's.

- To introduce (or set off) a defining or enumerating complementary element

  Early business centered about two important Air Force projects — the X-17 hypersonic ballistic missile and the X-7 — in order to flight-test ramjet engines and other components.

  A few days after V-J Day, President Robert Gross announced the receipt of aviation history's largest block of commercial orders for one company — 103 Constellations, valued at $75.5 million, from eight major airlines.

- To mark an interruption of thought or a sudden change of construction

  Except to a limited degree — Boeing had tentatively explored the "brand name" technique with the prewar Stratoliner — no aircraft manufacturer had ever before attempted to create full-scale ticket-buyer support.

---

*When the IBM Executive Typewriter with Bold Face No. 2 is used, 2 units are left before and after the dash in the first three usages given for the mark. In the fourth usage, when a range is indicated, 1 unit is left before and after the mark.

- To mark the omission of <u>to</u> or of <u>to and including</u> between dates, page numbers, and proper nouns used as a compound

pp. 4—30	2 June—30 December
New York—San Francisco flight	1956—1958

NOTE: The word <u>to</u> is used instead of the dash when <u>from</u> precedes the first quantity, when a range of scientific values is indicated, or when each quantity consists of two Arabic numerals separated by a hyphen.

pp. 10-1 to 10-14	from 10 to 15 cm/sec
from -24° to +8°F	from 2 June to 30 December

Chapter 13
SPELLING AND COMPOUNDING

The list given in this chapter comprises words for which more than one form is sanctioned by leading authorities. The purpose is to achieve consistency of usage. The list is not comprehensive; it consists chiefly of troublesome words that are likely to be used in technical publications. Included are (1) words that have more than one correct spelling (gage, gauge), and (2) words that may be hyphenated (pulse-jet), compounded (pulsejet), or used as separate units (pulse jet). All words listed represent a choice between sanctioned forms.

In selecting the particular forms of words included in this list, the increasing tendency to combine words as compounds, rather than to retain hyphens, has been considered. The prefixes identified in Chapter 12 as those not requiring a hyphen when joined to words are similarly handled in this chapter. The frequency of usage, or the likelihood of frequent usage, has been another criterion of selection. For example, with the increase in the number of atomic tests, fall-out has made the transition to fallout; and the transition of re-entry to reentry is anticipated.

Excluded from the list are words that are commonly misspelled and those that are commonly confused with other, similar words. The excluded categories are concerned simply with right and wrong usage rather than with a preference for one of several alternative forms.

For words that are not included in the list, Webster's New Collegiate Dictionary or the United States Government Printing Office Style Manual should be consulted. The GPO Style Manual is the primary authority on style for all government agencies (the chief customers for many companies) and contains lengthy chapters on spelling and compounding.

Combinations identified in parentheses as nouns and adjectives are written as two words when the first word is used as a verb; those identified as verbs and adjectives are written as two words when used as nouns.

acknowledgment
advisor
aforementioned
afterburner
aftereffect
airborne
airbreathing
airconditioned
airflow
airfoil
airframe
airtight
air-to-air
air-to-ground
alert-ready
align
analog
angle-of-attack
antiaircraft
antimaterial
antimissile
antipersonnel
antisubmarine
appendixes (not appendices)

backup (n., adj.)
bandwidth
beamwidth
bilateral
bimetallic
bimolecular
bipropellant
bistable
blackbody
bombproof
breadboard
breakdown (n., adj.)
breakthrough (n., adj.)
built-in (adj.)
builtup (adj.)
burnout (n., adj.)

busbar
buses
bypass
byproduct

callout (n., adj.)
cancel, -ed, -ing
candlepower
centerline
checkout (n., adj.)
closeup (n., adj.)
coexist
coordinate
countdown
counterbalance
counterclockwise
countermeasure
countermovement
crossover (n., adj.)
cross-sectional (but cross section)
cutback (n., adj.)
cutoff (n., adj.)
cutout (n., adj.)

data link
diagram, -med, -ming
disk

electrochemical
electromagnetic
electrooptical
endorse (not indorse)
enclose (not inclose)
end-product
equidistant

fallout (n., adj.)
feedback
ferroalloy
fireproof
flightpath

flight-test (v., adj.)
flip-flop
flowmeter
followon
followthrough (n., adj.)
followup (n., adj.)
formulas (not formulae)
freefall
freeflight
fuze (ordnance)

gage
gimbal
glidepath
go/no-go
gray
gyrocompass

heatproof
heatsink
heat-treat, -ing
height-finder
helixes (not helices)
horsepower
hotshot
humidity-proof

igniter
inboard
indexes (not indices)
infrared
input
install, -ed, -ing
interchangeable
interrelated

jetevator
jetstream
judgment

label, -ed, -ing
launch-pad
layout (n., adj.)
leakproof
lens, lenses
level, -ed, -ing

magnetohydrodynamics
manhour
manpower
manyear
matrices (not matrixes)
measurable
microhm
micrometeorite
micromicrosecond
microsecond
microvolt
microwave
milliampere
missileborne
mockup
model, -ed, -ing
moistureproof
monocoque
multiengine
multipurpose

narrowband
nonelectric
nonessential
nonexplosive
nonlethal
nonlinear
nonmetallic
nosecone
nosedive
nosedown

omnidirectional
omnirange
onboard
orbit, -ed, -ing
outboard
output
overall
overboard

payload
percent
phase-in
playback
polyethylene

polyform
polystyrene
powerplant
preflight
preventive (not preventative)
program, -med, -ming
pullout
pullup
pulsejet

radioactive
radioaltimeter
radiocompass
radiosonde
ramjet
rangefinder
readjust
readout
realign
reentry
retrorocket

satellite-tracking
self-pressurizing
self-starting
semiautomatic
semicircular
semienclosed
semi-independent
semipermeable
servocontrol
servomechanism
servomotor
servosystem
setup (n., adj.)
shockproof
sideband
sidewash
sizable
skycover
slipflow
slipstream
so-called
soundproof
spot-check (v., adj.)

state-of-the-art
subcontractor
subscript
subsonic
subsystem
subzero
sulfur
superaerodynamic
supercharge
superscript
supersonic
sweptback
sweptforward
sweptwing

tailwind
takeoff (n., adj.)
thrustpower
time-of-miss
total, -ed, -ing
toward (not towards)
transsonic
travel, -ed, -ing
troubleshooting
turbojet
turboprop
turboramjet
twofold

ultrahigh
ultrasonic
ultraviolet
underestimate
updraft
upgrade
up-to-date
upwash
usable

voltmeter
volt-ohmmeter

warhead
waterborne
waterproof

waveform
wavelength
weatherproof

wideband

zeroth-order

Chapter 14
NUMBERS

14.1 Use in the Mechanics of a Report

The numbers used in the mechanics of preparing a technical publication have already been considered in various chapters of this Guide. The numbering system for the divisions, pages, and illustrative materials of the technical publication has been discussed in some detail. For convenience, the salient points are brought together in the following summary.

Lowercase Roman numerals are used to paginate front matter. Arabic numerals are used to indicate the sequence of the following:

- Pages

- Sections, chapters, and sideheads

    Section 2

    Chapter 4

    2.1 Proofreading the Manuscript

    3.3.4 Preparation of Distribution List

- Figures and tables

    Fig. 14-3

    Table 15-2

- Equations

    Eq. (14.2)

    Eq. (A.3)

- Items of a listing

14.2 Use Within the Text

Technical publications obviously contain many quantitative concepts. These are expressed in Arabic numerals followed by units that are usually abbreviated. In the text, numbers are spelled out in certain instances (noted in the six examples below), and in all other instances they are in Arabic form.

A number is spelled out when it:

- Begins a sentence

  NOTE: Compound numbers are treated as unit modifiers and hence are hyphenated.

    Twenty-five

    Thirty-six

- Precedes a number which is the first element of a unit modifier

    six 5-ft posts

    two 2-cm bars

    three 20-channel units

- Is less than 10 and is not given with a unit

  NOTE: If a list includes a number greater than nine, no number is spelled out.

    three boys (but 3 cm)

    four quarterly reports and two monthly status reports

    5 nuts, 10 bolts, and 20 screws

- Is an ordinal number that is less than 10th and does not designate a unit

  NOTE: If a list includes a number greater than ninth, no number is spelled out.

    sixth (but 6th Army)

    26th

    the 2nd and the 14th chapters

- Would otherwise require the use of many zeros to express very large, nonscientific quantities

  NOTE: In such cases, millions or billions is spelled out and is preceded by the Arabic numeral.

    $418 billion (or 418 billion dollars)

    5.1 million Chinese

- Is a common fraction and is not followed by a unit

  NOTE: The hyphen is always used whether the fraction appears as a unit modifier or as a noun.

    a two-thirds majority

    three-fourths of the report (but 3/4-in. tube)

When numbers are used to express fractions:

- A zero is always placed before the decimal point of a simple decimal fraction.

- The number of digits after the decimal point specifies the precision of the value.

- A hyphen separates the integral and fractional parts of a mixed number when the fraction is written with a solidus.

    2-1/2 ft in diameter (but $2\frac{1}{2}$ ft long)

In precise scientific values, an Arabic numeral is used with powers of 10 to express:

- Very large numbers

    3×10^{10} cm/sec

- Very small numbers

    6.625×10^{-27} erg-sec

In-text numbers require:

- Commas when there are four or more digits

    2,459

- By rather than the times sign (×) in compound measurements

    2 by 4 by 8 ft

- Percent, in., ft, deg, No., rather than the symbols % , " , ' , ° , #

    NOTE: The degree symbol is used only for temperature measurements, spectroscopic terms, and geographic coordinates; the prime and double-prime symbols are used only for geographic coordinates.

    55 percent
    an angle of 10 deg
    -35° to +95° F
    40° 32'5" N

Dates are written without commas:

- When only the month and year are given

    March 1958

- When military style is used

    21 March 1958

Chapter 15
ABBREVIATIONS

15.1 Use of Abbreviations

Abbreviations are important. In modern technical writing, terminology can become so involved that the complete forms of expressions, repeated over and over, serve to impede rather than to aid comprehension. In technical publications, judicious use of commonly recognized abbreviations will help to make the meaning clear, to save the reader's time, and to maintain his interest.

There is no hard-and-fast rule for deciding when to use abbreviations. The author or editor may decide to adopt a given system of abbreviation for clarity or convenience. Once a system has been adopted, it must be followed consistently throughout the publication. Stylistic shifts (e.g., from $\underline{g/cm^2}$ to $\underline{g.-cm.^{-2}}$ or from $\underline{ft/sec}$ to $\underline{fps}$) only distract and may even annoy the careful reader. The meticulously edited scientific journals and the books of reputable technical publishers attest to professional recognition of the need for consistency in matters of style.

In general, abbreviations should be used only for one or more of the following reasons:

- When considerable space can be saved and cumbersome repetition avoided
- When the reader is more familiar with an abbreviation than with the complete form
- When use of an abbreviation is conventional

Abbreviations with which the reader is not familiar should be avoided. Such abbreviations should be defined when used for the first time.

Principles to observe in the use of abbreviations in text are as follows:

- Units of measurement (such as inch, mile, feet per second, and milli-microfarad) are usually abbreviated when used with numerals.
- No other abbreviations should be used except those which are well established for inclusion in text and those which are difficult to avoid because of the nature or frequency of the terms which they represent.
- Absolute consistency of usage should be maintained throughout the publication.

In tables and illustrations, where space is at a premium, abbreviations should be used freely. Units of measurement are rarely spelled out.

When an abbreviation for a unit consists of both capital and lowercase letters (e.g., Mc for megacycle) to avoid confusion with another abbreviation (mC for millicurie), the lowercase form is retained on callouts for illustrations, even though all other elements of the callouts are lettered in full capitals. (See Chapter 8.)

When followed by a number, the word Figure, Equation, or Reference is abbreviated if it does not begin a sentence. Table is never abbreviated, for it could be confused with tab. Abbreviations for Chapter and Section are not ordinarily used in text but may be used in footnotes, tables, illustrations, and bibliographies.

When names of months are abbreviated (e.g., in figures and tables), the first three letters of the name are used, without a period.

15.2 Compilation of Abbreviations

The list of abbreviations given on the following pages was compiled from a variety of sources representing different scientific and engineering disciplines. In many instances, these sources differ in their method of abbreviating compound units and in their choice of the simple unit abbreviations. Thus, $lb/in.^2$, or the more formal $lb\ per\ in.^2$, is used in the publications of one discipline, and the condensed form psi is found in those of another discipline. A number of alternative forms have been included in the list. Whenever possible, the author's choice of a particular form should be dictated by the usage of the recognized professional journals in his own field.

The style guides of the American Chemical Society, the American Institute of Physics, the Institute of Radio Engineers, and the American Standards Association have been followed for the majority of the entries in the list. In addition, representative government and industrial sources have been used.* The sources given with the entries have been coded as follows:

C	American Chemical Society
P	American Institute of Physics
S	American Standards Association
R	Institute of Radio Engineers
G	Governmental sources
I	Industrial laboratories
all	Agreement among at least four of the sources

No source has been shown for (1) commonly used abbreviations for nontechnical words (e.g., et al.), or (2) "abbreviations by fiat" for words or expressions that are too new to technical fields for abbreviations to have become widespread.

---

*Governmental sources comprise the United States Government Printing Office Style Manual, the Air Force Dictionary, Department of Defense listings, and the style guides of the U. S. Naval Ordnance Test Station and the U. S. Naval Radiological Defense Laboratory.

The form of the abbreviations for most nouns (e.g., lb, yd) is the same in both the singular and the plural. Exceptions include Refs., Figs., Nos., and Eqs. A period is used after an abbreviation for a unit of measurement only when the abbreviation spells out another complete word (e.g., in.) or otherwise might be mistaken for another word. A period usually follows an abbreviation for a general word.

In preparing the list of abbreviations for titles of periodicals, the lists and practices of Chemical Abstracts and the American Institute of Physics were used as standards. The abbreviations are in accordance with the principles of the standard lists.

Titles of periodicals are entered alphabetically by the first word unless the word is an article. Thus, titles beginning with Bulletin, Journal, Proceedings, and Transactions are listed under B, J, P, and T, respectively. This system of listing is consistent with that of leading physical-science journals. The system does not conform to that of technical libraries, which may or may not list a journal under the professional society that publishes it. A journal such as that of the Acoustical Society of America will appear as Acoustical Society of America, Journal of and is shelved under A rather than J. On the other hand, if the publication is sufficiently independent to warrant separate treatment, it is listed as Journal of ... .

The list of abbreviations is presented in four sections:

- Units of measurement
- General words
- Reference terms used in documentation
- Titles of periodicals

15.3 Units of Measurement

absolute ampere	abamp (P, G)	carat	spell out
acceleration due to gravity	g	centigram	cg (S)
acre	spell out (S, G)	centiliter	cl (P, S)
acre-foot	acre-ft (S)	centimeter	cm (P, G)
air horsepower	air hp (S, G)	centimeter-gram-second	cgs (P)
ampere	amp (all)	centimeter per second	cm/sec (G)
ampere-hour	amp-hr (P, G)	centipoise	cp (P, G)
ampere-turn	a-t (S, G)	circular mil(s)	cir mil (P, S, G)
amplitude (ellip. funct.)	am. (S, G)	continental horsepower	cont hp (S)
angstrom	A (all)	coulomb	spell out (P, S, G)
astronomical unit	AU	cubic centimeter (liq.)	cc (P, G)
atmosphere	atm (S, G)	cubic centimeter (vol.)	cm^3 (G)
atmosphere, standard	A_s (P)	cubic feet per minute	$cfm; ft^3/min$ (S, G)
atomic mass units	amu	cubic feet per second	$cfs; ft^3/sec$ (G)
atomic percent	at. %	cubic foot	$cu ft; ft^3$ (S)
		cubic inch	$cu in.; in.^3$ (G)
barn	b (P)	cubic meter	$cum; m^3$ (S, G)
barrel	bbl (S, G)	cubic micron	$cu\mu; \mu^3$ (S, G)
barye	spell out (P)	cubic millimeter	$cu mm; mm^3$ (S, G)
bel	spell out (R)	cubic yard	$cu yd; yd^3$ (S, G)
billion electron volts	Bev (P, G)	cycle	cy (P)
brake horsepower	bhp (S)	cycles per second	cps (P, S, G, R)
brake horsepower-hour	bhp-hr (P, G)		
British thermal unit	Btu (P, S, G)	day	spell out (G)
		decibel	db (all)
caliber	spell out (G)	decibel referred to 1 milliwatt	dbm (G)
calorie (small)	cal (P, S, G)	decibel referred to 1 volt	dbv (I)
Calorie (large)	Cal (P, G)	decibel referred to 1 watt	dbw (I)
candle	c (S)	degree (angular)	deg (P, S, G)*
candle-hour	c-hr (S, G)		
candlepower	cp (P, S, G)		

---

*The symbol ° is used for temperature measurements and for geographic coordinates.

degree centigrade (Celsius)	°C (P, G)	Gilbert	Gi (P)
degree Fahrenheit	°F (P, G)	gram	gm
degree Kelvin (absolute)	°K (P, G)	gram-calorie	g-cal (all)
degree Réaumur	°R (P, G)		
dozen	doz (G)	henry	h (all)
dyne	spell out	Hertz	He (P)
		horsepower	hp (all)
effective horsepower	ehp (G)	horsepower-hour	hp-hr (S, G)
electric horsepower	elhp (G)	hour	hr (all)
electromagnetic unit	emu (P, G)	hour (astron. tables)	h (S)
electromotive force	emf (all)	hundredweight	cwt (G)
electron volts	ev (P, G)		
electrostatic unit	esu (G)	inch	in. (all)
entropy unit	eu (P, G)	inches per second	ips;in./sec (S, G)
erg	spell out (P, G)	inch-pound	in.-lb (S, G)
		indicated horsepower	ihp (S, G)
farad	f (all)	indicated horsepower-hour	ihp-hr (S, G)
feet per minute	fpm;ft/min (S, G)	international angstrom	IA (P, G)
feet per second	fps;ft/sec (S, G)		
feet per second per second	ft/sec^2 (G)	joule	spell out (P)
foot	ft (all)		
foot-candle	ft-c (S, G)	kilocalorie	kcal (all)
foot-lambert	ft-L (S, G, P)	kilocycles per second	kc (P, S, G)
foot-pound	ft-lb (S, G, P)	kilo-electron-volt	kev (P, G)
foot-pound-second	ft-lb-sec (S)	kilogram	kg (all)
friction horsepower	fhp (G)	kilogram-calorie	kg-cal (G)
		kilogram-meter	kg-m (P, S, G)
gal (gravitational)	spell out	kilogram-weight	kg-wt (P)
gallons per minute	gpm;gal/min (S, G)	kilograms per cubic meter	kg/m^3 (G)
gallons per second	gps;gal/sec (S, G)	kilograms per second	kgps;kg/sec (P, S, G)
gauss	G (P)	kilojoule	kj (P, G)
gigacycle per second	Gc (R)	kiloliter	kl (P, S, G)

kilomegacycle per second	kMc (P, R)	microgram	μg (C, G)
kilometer	km (all)	microhenry	μh (G)
kilometers per second	kmps (S)	micromicrofarad	μμf (P, S, G)
kilopound	kip (S, G)	microinch	μin. (S, G)
kiloton	KT	micromicron	μμ (S, G)
kilovar	kvar (G)	micromole	μM (P, G)
kilovolt	kv (all)	micron	μ (all)
kilovolt-ampere	kva (all)	microreciprocal degrees Kelvin	μrd (G)
kilovolts peak	kvp (G)	microsecond	μsec (P, G)
kilowatt	kw (all)	microvolt	μv (S, G)
kilowatt-hour	kwhr;kw-hr (P, S, G)	microwatt	μw (S, G)
kips per square inch	ksi (G)	mil	spell out (G)
knot	spell out (G)	mile	mi (P, G)
		miles per hour	mph;mi/hr (P, S, G)
lambert	L (P, S, G)	milliampere	ma (all)
liter	l (P, S, G)	milliangstrom	mA (G)
lumen	lu (P, G)	millibar	mb
lumen-hour	lu-hr (G)	millibarn	mb
lumens per watt	lu/w	millicurie	mC (P, G)
		millicycles per second	mc (P, G)
Maxwell	Mx (P)	millifarad	mf (P, S)
mean horizontal candlepower	mhcp (all)	milligram	mg (all)
megacycles per second	Mc (P, G)	millihenry	mh (all)
megaton	MT	millilambert	mL (S, G)
megawatt	Mw (P, G)	milliliter	ml (all)
megohm	meg (P, G)	milli-mass-units	mmu (P)
meter	m (all)	millimeter	mm (all)
meter-kilogram	m-kg (S, G)	millimicrofarad	mμf (G)
mho	spell out (S, G)	millimicrogram	mμg;mγ (C)
microampere	μa (P, S, G)	millimicron	mμ (all)
microangstrom	μA (P, S, G)	millimicrosecond	mμsec (R)
microfarad	μf (P, S, G)	millimole	mM (P, G)

15-7

million electron volts	Mev (P, G)	pounds per square inch absolute	psia (S, G)
million volts	Mv (P, G)	pounds per square inch differential	psid
milliradian	mil (G)	pounds per square inch gage	psig
milliroentgen	mr (G)	pulses per second	pps
millisecond	ms (G)		
millivolt	mv (all)	quart	qt (S, G)
milliwatt	mw (G)		
minute (time and angular)	min (all)*	rad	spell out
minute (astron. tables)	m (S, G)	radian	spell out (S, G)
mole	M (P)	reactive kilovolt-ampere	kvar (S, G)
month	mo (G)	reactive volt-ampere	var (S, G)
		revolution	rev (G)
nanosecond	nsec (R)	revolutions per minute	rpm (all)
nautical mile	nm	revolutions per second	rps (all)
newton	N (P)	rod	spell out (S, G)
		roentgen	r (P, G)
ohm	spell out; Ω (P, R)	roentgen-equivalent-man	rem (G)
ohm-centimeter	ohm-cm (I)	roentgen-equivalent-physical	rep (G)
ounce	oz (all)		
ounce-foot	oz-ft (S, G)	second (time and angular)	sec (all)*
ounce-inch	oz-in.	second (astron. tables)	s (S, G)
		shaft horsepower	shp (S, G)
parts per million	ppm (S, G)	slug	spell out
picofarad	pf (R)	spherical candlepower	scp (S)
pint	pt (G)	square centimeter	sq cm;cm^2 (all)
poise	P (P)	square foot	sq ft;ft^2 (all)
pound	lb (all)	square inch	sq in. ;$in.^2$ (all)
pound-foot	lb-ft (S, G)	square kilometer	sq km;km^2 (all)
pounds per cubic foot	lb/ft^3 (G)	square meter	sq m;m^2 (P, S, G)
pounds per square foot	psf;lb/ft^2 (P, S, G)	square micron	μ^2 (P, S, G)
pounds per square inch	psi;$lb/in.^2$ (P, S, G)	square mile	sq mi (G)

---

*The symbol ' is used for geographic coordinates and may also be used on illustrations.

*The symbol " is used for geographic coordinates and may also be used on illustrations.

square millimeter	sq mm; mm^2 (S, G)	volt-coulomb	spell out
square yard	sq yd (G)	volt per meter	vpm (E)
stapp	spell out (G)	volume percent	vol %
statute mile	sm	volume unit	vu (R)
stere	st		
stereradian	sterad (P)	watt	w (all)
		watt-hour	w-hr (S, G)
teracycle per second	Tc (R)	watts per candle	wpc (S, G)
thousand pounds	kip (S, G)	week	wk (G)
ton	spell out (S, G)	weight percent	wt %
volt	v (all)	yard	yd (S, G)
volt-ampere	va (S, G)	year	yr (S, G)

15.4 General Words

absolute	abs. (C, S, G)	atomic weight	at. wt. (all)
acoustical	acous. (G)	audio frequency	af; AF (P, G, R)
addition	addn. (G)	automatic direction finder	ADF (R)
additional	addnl. (G)	automatic frequency control	AFC (R)
aerodynamic center	a. ctr. (all)	automatic gain control	AGC (I, R)
aeronautical	aeronaut.	automatic phase control	APC (R)
alcohol(ic)	alc. (C, G)	automatic volume control	AVC (I, R)
alkaline	alk. (C, G)	average	av. (C, P, G)
alkalinity	alky. (C, G)	avoirdupois	avoir. (G)
alternating current	ac; AC (P, R)	azimuth	az. (S, G)
altitude	alt. (P, G)		
amalgam	amal. (G)	boils at . . . °C	b. (C)
amorphous	amorph. (C, G)	balance	bal. (G)
amount	amt. (C, G)	barometer	bar. (G)
amplitude modulation	AM (G, R)	beat-frequency oscillator	BFO (I, R)
anhydrous	anhyd. (C, G)	beating oscillator	BO (R)
answer	ans. (G)	boiling point	b. p. (C, G)
ante meridian	a. m.; A. M. (all)	brake mean effective pressure	b. m. e. p. (S)
antilogarithm	antilog (P, G)	brake specific fuel consumption	b. s. f. c. (S)
apparatus	app. (C, G)	Brinnell hardness number	B. h. n. (S, G)
applied	appl. (G)	broadcast	bc; BC (R)
approximate(ly)	approx. (all)		
aqueous	aq. (C, G)	calculated	calcd. (C, G)
armature	arm. (I)	calculating	calcg. (C, G)
associate, association	assoc. (C, G)	calculation	calcn. (C, G)
associated	assocd. (C, G)	capacitor	cap. (I)
astronomical	astron.	cathode-ray oscilloscope	CRO (G, R)
atomic	at. (G)	cathode-ray tube	CRT (G, R)
atomic mass units	amu (P)	centerline	CL
atomic number	at. no. (G)	center of buoyancy	c. b. (G)

center of gravity	c. g. ; CG (all)	corporation	corp. (G)
center of impact	CI	counter electromotive force	c. e. m. f. ; CEMF (G)
centigrade	C (all)	critical	crit. (C, G)
center of mass	c. m. (P)	crystalline	cryst. (C, G)
center of pressure	cp; CP (S, G)	crystallization	crystn. (C, G)
center to center	c. to c. (G)	crystallized	crystd. (C, G)
centimeter-gram-second (system)	cgs (P, G)	crystallizing	crystg. (C, G)
chemically pure	c. p. (C, G)	crystal oscillator	CO (I)
chord	cd. (G)	current density	c. d. (P, G)
circuit	cir. (I)	cycle	spell out (P)
circular	circ.	cylinder, cylindrical	cyl. (S, G)
circular error average	CEA (G)		
circular probable error	CEP (G)	dark	dk. (G)
circumference	circum. (G)	day	spell out (S)
coefficient	coeff. (C, P)	decompose(s)	decomp. (C, G)
cologarithm	colog (P)	decomposed	decompd. (C, G)
commercial	com. (C, G)	decomposing	decompg. (C, G)
composition	compn. (C, G)	decomposition	decompn. (C, G)
compound	compd. (C, G)	definition(s)	def. (G)
compression ratio	c. r. (G)	deflection probable error	DEP (G)
concentrate	conc. (C, S, G)	derivative	deriv. (C, G)
concentrated	concd. (C, G)	desired ground zero	DGZ (G)
concentrating	concg. (C, G)	desired mean point of impact	DMPI (G)
concentration	conc. (C, G)	determine	det. (C, G)
condenser	cond. (I)	determined	detd. (C, G)
conductivity	conduct.	determining	detg. (C, G)
constant	const. (all)	determination	detn. (C, G)
contact potential difference	c. p. d. (F)	dew point	d. p. (I)
containing	contg. (C, G)	diameter	diam. ; D (all)
continuous wave	CW (R)	differential ballistic wind	d. b. w. (G)
coordinate, coordination	coord. (G)	dilute	dil. (C, G)
correct(ed)	cor. (G)	diluted	dild. (C, G)

dilution	diln. (C, G)	explodes	exp. (G)
direct current	dc; DC (P, R)	exponent	exp (all)
direction finder	DF (I, G)	external(ly)	extl. (C)
dissociate(s)	dissoc. (C, G)	extract	ext. (C, G)
dissociated	dissocd. (C, G)	extracted	extd. (C, G)
dissociation	dissocn. (C, G)	extraction	extn. (C, G)
distilled	distd. (C, G)	extremely high frequency	EHF (G, R)
distilling	distg. (C, G)	extremely low frequency	ELF (R)
distillation	distn. (C, G)		
double-pole (switch)	DP (G)	firing error indicator	FEI
double-pole double-throw (switch)	DPDT (G)	flight control system	FCS
double sideband	DSB (R)	fluid	fl. (C)
		fluorescent	fluores. (G)
efficiency	eff. (S)	foot-pound-second (system)	fps
elastic center	e. c. (G)	freezing point	f. p. (C, G)
elastic limit	e. l. (I)	frequency modulation	FM (P, G, R)
electric(al)	elec. (C, S, G)	fusion point	fn. p. (I)
electromotive force	e. m. f.; EMF (C, S, G)		
elevation	el. (S, G)	gage	ga. (G)
equilibrium(s)	equil. (C, G)	general	gen. (G)
equivalent	equiv. (C, G)	glacial	glac. (G)
estimate	est. (C, G)	glycerin	glyc. (C, G)
estimated	estd. (C, G)	grain	spell out (C, G)
estimating	estg. (C, G)	ground	gnd. (G)
evaporate	evap. (C, G)	ground-controlled intercept	GCI (G, R)
evaporated	evapd. (C, G)	ground-controlled approach	GCA (G, R)
evaporation	evapn. (C, G)	ground-position indicator	GPI (G, R)
evaporating	evapg. (C, G)		
examining	examg. (C, G)	hexagon(al)	hex. (G)
examination	examn. (G)	high frequency	HF (R, G)
experiment	expt. (C, G)	hygroscopic	hyg. (G)
experimental	exptl. (C, G)	hyperfine structure	h. f. s. (P)

identification, friend or foe	IFF (G, R)	manufacturing	mfg. (G)
ignition	ign. (G)	mass	spell out (S)
impedance	imp. (I)	mathematical	math. (C, G)
indicated air speed	IAS (G)	maximum	max. (all)
inductance-capacitance	LC (I, R)	maximum permissible exposure	m. p. e. (G)
induction	induc. (G)	maximum usable frequency	MUF (R)
infrared	IR (R)	mean effective pressure	m. e. p. (S, G)
initial temperature difference	i. t. d. ; ITD (G)	mean free path	m. f. p. (G)
initial point	IP (G)	mean point of impact	MPI (G)
inside diameter	i. d. ; ID (P, S, R)	mechanical	mech. (G)
insoluble	insol. (C)	median lethal dose	LD_{50} (G)
intermediate frequency	IF (R, G)	medium	med. (G)
internal	int. (S, G)	medium frequency	MF (R, G)
interrupted continuous wave	ICW (R)	melting point	mp (P, S)
isometric	isom. (S, G)	metallurgy, metallurgical	metall. (G)
isotropic	iso. (C, G)	meter-kilogram-second (system)	mks (P, G)
isothermal	isoth. (G)	milliequivalent	meq. (C)
		minimum	min. (all)
kinetic energy	KE (P)	miscellaneous	misc. (G)
		missile station	M. S.
latitude	lat. (S, G)	modulated continuous wave	MCW (G, R)
leading edge	l. e. (G)	molar	$\underline{M}$ (C, P, G)
limit	lim.	molecular weight	mol. wt. (G)
limit (mathematics)	lim	molecule	mol. (C, G)
limited	ltd.	monoclinic	monocl. (G)
linear	lin. (S, G)	month	mo. (G)
liquid	liq. (S, G)		
longitude	long. (S, G)	negative	neg. (C, G)
low frequency	LF (R, G)	nitrocellulose	NC (G)
		nitroglycerin	NG (G)
magazine	mag. (G)	normal (direction)	norm. (G)
magnetomotive force	m. m. f. (P)	normal	$\underline{N}$ (C, G)

nuclear magneton	n. m. (P)	pressure-volume-temperature	PVT (P, G)
Number(s)	No(s). (P, G)	prism(s)	pr. (G)
		progress	prog. (G)
observed	obs. (P, S, G)	pulse-amplitude modulation	PAM (I, G)
octahedral	octahdr. (G)	pulse-code modulation	PCM (I)
organic	org. (C, G)	pulse-duration modulation	PDM (R)
orthorhombic (crystallography)	orhomb. (G)	pulse-position modulation	PPM (R)
outside diameter	od; OD (P. S)	pulse-time modulation	PTM (G, I)
		pulse-width modulation	PWM (I, R)
perpendicular	perp. (G)		
phase	ph. (G)	quadrant elevation	QE (G)
phase modulation	PM (R)	qualitative	qual. (C, G)
physical	phys. (C, G)	quantitative	quant. (C, G)
physiological	physiol. (C, G)		
plan-position indicator	PPI (G, R)	radio direction finder	RDF (G, R)
point	pt. (G)	radio frequency	rf; RF (P, G)
positive	pos. (G)	radio frequency interference	RFI (R)
post meridian	p. m. ; P. M. (all)	radius	rad. ; R (G)
potential	spell out	range error probability	REP (G)
potential difference	PD (P)	regular	reg. (G)
potential energy	PE (R)	relative biological effectiveness	RBE
powdered	powd. (C, G)	relative humidity	RH (G)
power amplifier	PA (G)	resistance-capacitance	RC (I)
power factor	pf; PF (S, R)	respectively	resp. (C, G)
precipitate	ppt. (C, G)	rhombic	rhomb. (G)
precipitated	pptd. (C, G)	right hand	r. h. (G)
precipitating	pptg. (C, G)	root mean square	rms (P, S, G)
precipitation	pptn. (C, G)	root sum square	rss (R)
preparation	prepn. (C, G)		
prepare	prep. (C, G)	saturate	sat. (C, G)
prepared	prepd. (C, G)	saturated	satd. (C, G)
pressure	press. (G)	saturating	satg. (C, G)

separate	sep. (C, G)	tetragonal	tetr. (G)
separating	sepg. (C, G)	transmit-receive	TR (R)
separation	sepn. (C, G)	transverse electromagnetic	TEM (R)
short wave	SW (R)	traveling wave	tw; TW (G, R)
sidereal hour angle	s.h.a. (G)	triclinic	tricl. (G)
signal-to-noise ratio	SNR (R)	trinitrotoluene	TNT (G)
single-pole (switch)	SP (G)	triple-pole (switch)	3P (G)
single sideband	SSB (R)	true air speed	tas; TAS
slightly	sl. (C, G)	true azimuth	Zn (G)
soluble	sol. (C, G)	true heading	t.h. (G)
solution	soln. (C, G)	tuned radio frequency	TRF (R)
specific gravity	sp.gr. (C, S, G)		
specific heat	sp.ht. (C, S, G)	ultrahigh frequency	UHF (P, R, G)
specific volume	sp.vol. (C, G)		
square	sq. (P, S, G)	vacuum-tube voltmeter	VTVM (R)
standard	std. (S, G)	variable-frequency oscillator	VFO (R)
standing-wave ratio	SWR (R)	velocity	vel. (G)
superhigh frequency	SHF (G, R)	versus	vs.
switch	sw.; SW (G)	very-high frequency	VHF (R, G)
symmetrical	sym. (C, G)	very-high-frequency omnidirectional radio range	VOR (R)
synopsis, synoptic	synop. (G)	very-low frequency	VLF (R, G)
		vestigial sideband	VSB (R)
television	TV (R)	viscosity	visc. (C, G)
temperature	temp. (C, S, G)	voltage regulator	VR (R)
tensile strength	t.s. (S, G)	voltage standing wave ratio	VSWR (R)
terrain-clearance indicator	TCI (R)		

15.5 Reference Terms Used in Documentation

abstract	abst.	no date	n.d.
anonymous	anon.	no page	n.p.
article	Art.	note	n.
		Number (journal)	No.
bibliography	biblio.		
		paragraph(s)	par(s).
chapter(s)	Ch(s).	page	p.
column	Col.	pages	pp.
compare (confere)	cf.	part	Pt.
compiler, compiled	comp.	plate	Pl.
continued	cont.	proceedings	Proc.
copyright	c.	published, publisher	publ.
		publication(s)	pub(s).
editor(s)	ed(s).		
edition	ed.	reference(s)	Ref(s).
equation(s)	Eq(s).	respectively	resp.
especially	esp.	review	Rev.
		revised	revd.
figure(s)	Fig(s).		
following (page)	f.	section	Sec.
following (pages)	ff.	series	Ser.
footnote	fn.	supplement(s)	Supp(s).
frontispiece	frontis.		
		table	Table
illustration	illus.	transactions	Trans.
inclusive	incl.	translated, translation	tr.
journal	J.	university	univ.
manuscript(s)	MS(S)	volume(s)	Vol(s).

Latin Reference Terms

ca. (circa)	about	loc. cit. (loco citato)	in the place cited
cf. (confere)	compare	n.b. (nota bene)	note well
et al. (et alii)	and others	op. cit. (opere citato)	in the work cited
etc. (et cetera)	and so forth	passim (spell out)	here and there
e.g. (exempli gratia)	for example	q.v. (quod vide)	which see
et seq. (et sequens)	and the following	sic (spell out)	thus
ibid. (ibidem)	in the same place	viz. (videlicet)	namely
i.e. (id est)	that is	vs. (versus)	against
infra (spell out)	below		

15.6 Titles of Periodicals

Acta Chemica Scandinavica	Acta Chem. Scand.
Acta Chimica Academiae Scientiarum Hungaricae	Acta Chim. Acad. Sci. Hung.
Acta Crystallographica	Acta Cryst.
Acta Mathematica	Acta Math.
Acta Metallurgica	Acta Met.
Acta Physica Academiae Scientiarum Hungaricae	Acta Phys. Acad. Sci., Hung.
Acta Physica Austriaca	Acta Phys. Austriaca
Acta Technica Academiae Scientiarum Hungaricae	Acta Tech. Acad. Sci. Hung.
Acustica	Acustica
Advances in Chemistry	Adv. in Chem.
Advances in Electronics and Electron Physics	Adv. in Electronics and Electron Phys.
Advances in Physics	Adv. in Phys.
Aerospace Engineering	Aerospace Eng.
Aerospace Medicine	Aerospace Med.
Aeronautical Quarterly	Aeronaut. Quart.
Âge Nucléaire, Le	Âge Nucléaire
Aircraft (Canada)	Aircraft (Canada)
Aircraft Engineering	Aircraft Eng.
Aircraft and Missiles Manufacturing	Aircraft Miss. Manuf.
Air University Quarterly Review	Air Univ. Quart. Rev.
Akademiya Nauk S.S.S.R. Inst.	Akad. Nauk S.S.S.R. Inst.
Akustische Zeitschrift	Akust. Z.
American Aviation	Am. Aviat.
American Documentation	Am. Document.
American Institute of Chemical Engineers Journal	Am. Inst. Chem. Engrs. J. (colloq.: A.I.Ch.E.J.)
American Journal of Mathematics	Am. J. Math.

American Journal of Physics	Am. J. Phys.
American Journal of Psychology	Am. J. Psych.
American Mathematical Monthly	Am. Math. Month.
Analyst	Analyst
Analytical Chemistry	Anal. Chem.
Analytica Chimica Acta	Anal. Chim. Acta
Angewandte Chemie	Angew. Chem.
Annalen der Chemie, Justus Liebigs	Ann. Chem. Liebigs (colloq.: Ann.)
Annalen der Physik	Ann. P.
Annales de chimie (Paris)	Ann. chim. (Paris)
Annales de géophysique	Ann. géophys.
Annales de physique	Ann. phys.
Annales de télécommunications	Ann. telecomm.
Annals of the International Geophysical Year	Ann. IGY
Annals of Mathematical Statistics	Ann. Math. Stat.
Annals of Mathematics	Ann. Math.
Annals of Physics	Ann. Phys.
Annual Review of Physical Chemistry	Ann. Rev. Phys. Chem.
Applied Hydraulics	Appl. Hydraulics
Applied Mechanics Reviews	Appl. Mech. Rev.
Applied Scientific Research	Appl. Sci. Res.
Applied Spectroscopy	Appl. Spectroscopy
Arkiv för Fysik	Arkiv Fys.
Archiv für Elektrotechnik	Arch. Elektrotech.
Archiv der Mathematik	Arch. Math.
Archiv für Meteorologie, Geophysik und Bioklimatologie	Arch. Meteorol. Geophys. u. Bioklimatol.
ARS Journal	ARS J.
ASTM Bulletin	ASTM Bull.
Astronautica Acta	Astron. Acta
Astronautics	Astronautics

Astronomical Journal	Astron. J.
Astronomicheskiĭ Zhurnal	Astron. Zhur.
Astrophysical Journal	Astrophys. J.
Atomics and Nuclear Energy	At. and Nucl. Energy
Australian Journal of Applied Science	Australian J. Appl. Sci.
Australian Journal of Chemistry	Australian J. Chem.
Australian Journal of Physics	Australian J. Phys.
Automatic Control	Automat. Cont.
Automation	Automation
Automation and Remote Control (Avtomatika i Telemekanika, Doklad, Akad. Nauk, U.S.S.R.)	Auto. and Rem. Cont. (U.S.S.R.)
Battelle Technical Review	Battelle Tech. Rev.
Beitrage zür Physik der Atmosphäre	Beit. Phys. Atmos.
Bell System Technical Journal	Bell System Tech. J.
Berichte der deutschen chemischen Gesellschaft	Ber. deut. chem. Ges. (or Ber.)
Berichte der deutschen physikalischen Gesellschaft	Ber. deut. physik. Ges.
Biochemical Journal	Biochem. J.
Biochemische Zeitschrift	Biochem. Z.
Biochimica et Biophysica Acta	Biochim. et Biophys. Acta
Biokhimiya	Biokhimiya
British Journal of Applied Physics	Brit. J. Appl. Phys.
British Journal of Radiology	Brit. J. Radiol.
British Plastics	Brit. Plastics
Bulletin of the Academy of Sciences of the U.S.S.R.	Bull. Acad. Sci. U.S.S.R.
Bulletin of the Academy of Sciences U.S.S.R. Division of Chemical Science (Eng. tr.)	Bull. Acad. Sci. U.S.S.R. Div. Chem. Sci.
Bulletin of the American Ceramic Society	Bull. Am. Ceram. Soc.
Bulletin of the American Institute of Mining and Metallurgical Engineers	Bull. Am. Inst. Mining Met. Engrs. (colloq.: Bull. AIME)
Bulletin of the American Mathematical Society	Bull. Am. Math. Soc.
Bulletin of the American Meteorological Society	Bull. Am. Meteorol. Soc.

Bulletin of the American Physical Society	Bull. Am. Phys. Soc.
Bulletin of the Bureau of Standards	Bull. Bur. Standards
Bulletin of the Chemical Society of Japan	Bull. Chem. Soc. Japan
Bulletin of the Geological Society of America	Bull. Geol. Soc. Am.
Bulletin of the Lick Observatory	Bull. Lick Observ.
Bulletin of Mathematical Biophysics	Bull. Math. Biophys.
Bulletin des sciences mathématiques	Bull. sci. math.
Bulletin de la société chimique de France	Bull. soc. chim. France
Bulletin de la société mathématique de France	Bull. soc. math. France
Canadian Journal of Chemistry	Can. J. Chem.
Canadian Journal of Mathematics	Can. J. Math.
Canadian Journal of Physics	Can. J. Phys.
Canadian Journal of Research	Can. J. Res.
Canadian Journal of Technology	Can. J. Technol.
Canadian Mining and Metallurgical Bulletin	Can. Mining Met. Bull.
Ceramic Age	Ceram. Age
Ceramic Industry	Ceram. Ind.
Chemical Abstracts	Chem. Abstracts (colloq. in Chem. Abstracts: C.A.)
Chemical Engineering	Chem. Eng.
Chemical Engineering Progress	Chem. Eng. Prog.
Chemical Reviews	Chem. Revs.
Chemiker-Zeitung	Chemiker-Z.
Chemische Berichte	Chem. Ber.
Chemisches Zentralblatt	Chem. Zentr.
Chimie & industrie (Paris)	Chim. & ind. (Paris)
Combustion and Flame	Comb. and Flame
Communications on Pure and Applied Mathematics	Commun. Pure Appl. Math.
Compositio Mathematica	Compositio Math.

Comptes rendus hebdomadaires des séances de l'académie des sciences	Compt. rend.
Computer Journal, The	Comput. J.
Computers and Automation	Comput. and Automat.
Control Engineering	Control Eng.
Corrosion	Corrosion
Daedalus	Daedalus
Datamation	Datamat.
Data Processing Digest	Data Process. Dig.
Deep-Sea Research	Deep-Sea Res.
Discussions of the Faraday Society	Discussions Faraday Soc.
Doklady Akademii Nauk S.S.S.R.	Doklady Akad. Nauk S.S.S.R.
Duke Mathematical Journal	Duke Math. J.
Electrical Communication	Elect. Commun.
Electrical Engineering	Elect. Eng.
Electromechanical Design	Electromech. Des.
Electronic Design	Electronic Des.
Electronic Engineering	Electronic Eng.
Electronic Industries and Tele-Tech	Electronic Ind. Tele-Tech
Electronic and Radio Engineer	Electronic Radio Engr.
Electronics	Electronics
Electrotechnische Zeitschrift	Electrotech. Z.
Endeavour	Endeavour
Engineer, The	Engineer
Engineering and Science	Eng. Sci.
Environmental Quarterly	Environ. Quart.
Ergebnisse der exakten Naturwissenschaften	Ergeb. exakt. Naturwiss.
Experientia	Experientia
Explosivstoffe	Explosivst.

Fortschritte der chemischen Forschung	Fortschr. chem. Forsch.
Gazzetta chimica italiana	Gazz. chim. ital.
Geological Magazine	Geol. Mag.
Geologie (Berlin)	Geologie (Berlin)
Geologische Rundschau	Geol. Rundschau
Geophysical Journal	Geophys. J.
Geophysics	Geophysics
Gerlands Beiträge zur Geophysik	Gerlands Beitr. Geophys.
Health Physics	Health Phys.
Helvetica Chimica Acta	Helv. Chim. Acta
Helvetica Physica Acta	Helv. Phys. Acta
IBM Journal of Research and Development	IBM J. Res. Dev.
IGY Bulletin	IGY Bull.
Illinois Journal of Mathematics	Illinois J. Math.
Indagationes Mathematicae	Indagationes Math.
Indian Journal of Physics	Indian J. Phys.
Industrial and Applied Mathematics	Indust. Appl. Math.
Industrial and Engineering Chemistry	Ind. Eng. Chem.
Industrial Hygiene	Ind. Hyg.
Information and Control	Inform. Control
Ingenieur-Archiv	Ingr.-Arch.
Inorganic Syntheses	Inorg. Syntheses
Institute of Metals (London) Monograph and Report Series	Inst. Metals (London) Monograph and Rep. Ser.
Instrument Society of America Journal	ISA J.
Instruments	Instruments
Instruments and Automation	Instr. and Automation
Interavia	Interavia

International Journal of Applied Radiation and Isotopes	Intern. J. Appl. Radiation and Isotopes
Iron Age, The	Iron Age
Izvestiya Akademii Nauk S.S.S.R. (For bulletins of the Academy of Sciences of the U.S.S.R., supply subject and series identification. For English translations, see under Bulletin of the Academy of Sciences, U.S.S.R.)	Isvest. Akad. Nauk S.S.S.R.
Japanese Journal of Geophysics	Japan. J. Geophys.
Japanese Journal of Physics	Japan. J. Phys.
Journal of the Acoustical Society of America	J. Acoust. Soc. Am.
Journal of the Aerospace Sciences	J. Aerospace Sci.
Journal of the American Ceramic Society	J. Am. Ceram. Soc.
Journal of the American Chemical Society	J. Am. Chem. Soc. (colloq.: JACS)
Journal of the American Institute of Electrical Engineers	J. Am. Inst. Elec. Engr. (colloq.: JAIEE)
Journal of the American Institute of Metals	J. Am. Inst. Metals
Journal of the American Medical Association	J. Am. Med. Assoc.
Journal of the American Welding Society	J. Am. Weld. Soc.
Journal of Analytical Chemistry of the U.S.S.R. (Eng. tr.)	J. Anal. Chem. U.S.S.R.
Journal of Applied Chemistry (London)	J. Appl. Chem. (London)
Journal of Applied Chemistry of the U.S.S.R. (Eng. tr.)	J. Appl. Chem. U.S.S.R.
Journal of Applied Mechanics	J. Appl. Mech.
Journal of Applied Physics	J. Appl. Phys.
Journal of the Association for Computing Machinery	J. Assoc. Comput. Mach.
Journal of Astronautics	J. Astronaut.
Journal of Atmospheric & Terrestrial Physics	J. Atmos. Terrest. Phys.
Journal of Biological Chemistry	J. Biol. Chem.
Journal of the British Institution of Radio Engineers	J. Brit. Inst. Radio Engrs.
Journal of the British Interplanetary Society	J. Brit. Interplanet. Soc.
Journal of Chemical and Engineering Data	J. Chem. Eng. Data
Journal of Chemical Physics	J. Chem. Phys.

Journal of the Chemical Society (London)	J. Chem. Soc. (London)
Journal of Colloid Science	J. Colloid Sci.
Journal of Documentation, The	J. Document.
Journal of the Electrochemical Society	J. Electrochem. Soc.
Journal of Electronics	J. Electronics
Journal of Experimental Physiology	J. Exptl. Physiol.
Journal of Fluid Mechanics	J. Fluid Mech.
Journal of the Franklin Institute	J. Franklin Inst.
Journal of General Physiology	J. Gen. Physiol.
Journal of Geophysical Research	J. Geophys. Res.
Journal of the Indian Institute of Science	J. Indian Inst. Sci.
Journal of Inorganic & Nuclear Chemistry	J. Inorg. & Nuclear Chem.
Journal of the Institute of Electrical Engineers of Japan	J. Inst. Elec. Engrs. Japan
Journal of the Institute of Metals	J. Inst. Metals
Journal of the Institution of Electrical Engineers (London)	J. Inst. Elec. Engrs. (London)
Journal of the London Mathematical Society	J. London Math. Soc.
Journal of the Mathematical Society of Japan	J. Math. Soc. Japan
Journal of Mathematics and Mechanics	J. Math. and Mech.
Journal of Mathematics and Physics	J. Math. and Phys.
Journal de mathématiques pures et appliquées	J. math. pures et appl.
Journal of the Mechanics and Physics of Solids	J. Mech. and Phys. Solids
Journal of Metallurgy and Ceramics	J. Met. and Ceram.
Journal of Metals	J. Metals
Journal of Meteorology, The	J. Meteorol.
Journal of Neurophysiology	J. Neurophysiol.
Journal of Nuclear Energy	J. Nuclear Energy
Journal of the Optical Society of America	J. Opt. Soc. Am.
Journal of Organic Chemistry, The	J. Org. Chem.
Journal of Photographic Science	J. Phot. Sci.
Journal of Physical Chemistry	J. Phys. Chem.

Journal of the Physical Society of Japan	J. Phys. Soc. Japan
Journal of Physics (U.S.S.R.)	J. Phys. (U.S.S.R.)
Journal de physique, et le radium	J. phys. radium
Journal de physique et le radium, physique appliqué	J. phys. radium, phys. appl.
Journal of Polymer Science	J. Polymer Sci.
Journal für praktische Chemie	J. prakt. Chem.
Journal of Rational Mechanics and Analysis	J. Rational Mech. and Analysis
Journal für die reine und angewandte Mathematik	J. reine u. angew. Math.
Journal of Research of the National Bureau of Standards	J. Res. Natl. Bur. Standards (or J. Res. NBS)
Journal of Rheology	J. Rheol.
Journal of the Royal Aeronautical Society	J. Roy. Aeronaut. Soc.
Journal of the Russian Physical-Chemical Society	J. Russ. Phys.-Chem. Soc.
Journal of Scientific Instruments	J. Sci. Instr.
Journal of the Society of Glass Technology	J. Soc. Glass Technol.
Journal of the Society for Industrial and Applied Mathematics	J. Soc. Indust. and Appl. Math.
Journal of the Society of Plastics Engineers	J. Soc. Plastics Engrs.
Journal of Technical Physics (U.S.S.R.)	J. Tech. Phys. (U.S.S.R.)
Khimicheskaya Nauka i Promyshlennost	Khim. Nauka i Prom.
Khimicheskaya Promyshlennost	Khim. Prom.
Koninklijke Nederlandse Akademie van Wetenschappen, Proceedings	Koninkl. Ned. Akad. Wetenschap. Proc.
Laboratory, The	Laboratory
Machine Design	Machine Des.
Machinery	Machinery
Makromolekulare Chemie	Makromol. Chem.
Marconi Review	Marconi Rev.

Materials Handling	Materials Handl.
Materials & Methods	Mater. & Meth.
Mathematical Reviews	Math. Rev.
Mathematical Tables and Other Aids to Computation	Math. Tables
Mathematics Magazine	Math. Mag.
Mathematische Annalen	Math. Annal.
Mathematische Nachrichten	Math. Nachr.
Matematicheskiĭ Sbornik	Mat. Sbornik
Mechanical Engineering	Mech. Eng.
Mémoires de l'académie polonaise des sciences et des lettres. Classe des sciences mathématiques et naturelles	Mem. acad. polon. sci. Classe sci. math. et nat.
Memorias y revista de la academia nacional de ciencias (Mexico)	Mem. y rev. acad. nac. cienc. (Mex.)
Mesures et controle industriel	Mesures et controle indust.
Metal Finishing	Metal Finish.
Metallurgia	Metallurgia
Metallurgical Abstracts	Met. Abstr.
Metallurgical Reviews	Met. Rev.
Metal Progress	Metal Progr.
Metals Review	Metals Rev.
Meteoritics	Meteoritics
Meteorological Magazine, The	Meteorol. Mag.
Météorologie, La	Météorologie
Meteorologische Rundschau	Meteorol. Rundschau
Metody i Protsessy Khimicheskoĭ Tekhnologii, Akademiya Nauk S.S.S.R.	Metody i Protsessy Khim. Tekhnol. Akad. Nauk S.S.S.R.
Microtecnic	Microtecnic
Military Automation	Mil. Automat.
Military Electronics	Mil. Electron.
Military Engineer	Mil. Engr.
Mining and Metallurgy	Mining and Met.

Missile Design and Development	Missile Des. and Dev.
Missiles and Rockets	Miss. and Rock.
Modern Materials Handling	Mod. Mater. Handl.
Modern Metals	Mod. Metals
Modern Packaging	Mod. Packag.
Modern Plastics	Mod. Plastics
Monatshefte für Chemie	Monatsh. Chem.
Monatshefte für Mathematik	Monatsh. Math.
Nachrichten der Akademie der Wissenschaften in Göttingen, Mathematisch-physikalische Klasse	Nachr. Akad. Wiss. Göttingen Math.-phys. Kl.
National Aeronautics and Space Administration, Technical Publications Announcements	Nat. Aeronaut. and Space Admin. (or NASA), Tech. Pub. Announ.
National Bureau of Standards (U.S.), Technical News Bulletin	Nat. Bur. Standards (U.S.) (or NBS) Tech. News Bull.
Nature	Nature
Naturwissenschaften, Die	Naturwiss.
Nuclear Engineering	Nuclear Eng.
Nuclear Instruments	Nuclear Inst.
Nuclear Physics	Nuclear Phys.
Nuclear Power	Nuclear Power
Nuclear Science and Engineering	Nuclear Sci. Eng.
Nucleonics	Nucleonics
Nukleonik	Nukleonik
Numerische Mathematik	Num. Math.
Nuovo cimento	Nuovo cimento
Observatory, The	Observatory
Oesterreichische Akademie der Wissenschaften, Mathematisch-naturwissenschaftliche Klasse, Sitzungsberichte	Oesterr. Akad. Wiss. Math.-naturw. Kl. Sitz. ber.

Office of Naval Research, Research Reviews	Office Naval Research (or ONR) Res. Rev.
Onde Électrique, Le	Onde Elect.
Operations Research	Operations Res.
Optica Acta (Paris)	Optica Acta (Paris)
Optik	Optik
Ordnance	Ordnance
Pacific Journal of Mathematics	Pacific J. Math.
Philips Research Reports	Philips Res. Rep.
Philosophical Magazine	Phil. Mag.
Philosophical Transactions of the Royal Society (London)	Trans. Roy. Soc. (London)
Photographic Science and Technique	Photo. Sci. Tech.
Photographic Journal	Photo. J.
Physica	Physica
Physical Review	Phys. Rev.
Physical Review Letters	Phys. Rev. Let.
Physics and Chemistry of Solids, The	Phys. and Chem. Solids
Physics of Fluids	Phys. Fluids
Physics of Metals and Metallography	Phys. Metals and Metallog.
Physics Today	Phys. Today
Physik	Physik
Physikalische Berichte	Physik. Ber.
Physikalische Zeitschrift	Physik. Z.
Physikalische Zeitschrift der Sowjetunion	Physik. Z. Sowjetunion
Plastics	Plastics
Plating	Plating
Powder Metallurgy Bulletin	Powder Met. Bull.
Power Reactor Technology	Power Reactor Technol.
Priroda	Priroda

Product Engineering	Prod. Eng.
Proceedings of the American Mathematical Society	Proc. Am. Math. Soc.
Proceedings of the American Philosophical Society	Proc. Am. Phil. Soc.
Proceedings of the American Society for Testing Materials	Proc. Am. Soc. Testing Materials (or Proc. ASTM)
Proceedings of the Cambridge Philosophical Society	Proc. Cambridge Phil. Soc.
Proceedings of the Edinburgh Mathematical Society	Proc. Edinburgh Math. Soc.
Proceedings of the Indian Academy of Sciences	Proc. Indian Acad. Sci.
Proceedings of the Institute of Radio Engineers	Proc. Inst. Radio Engrs. (colloq.: Proc. IRE)
Proceedings of the Institution of Electrical Engineers (London)	Proc. Inst. Elec. Engrs. (London)
Proceedings of the Institution of Mechanical Engineers (London)	Proc. Inst. Mech. Engrs. (London)
Proceedings of the London Mathematical Society	Proc. London Math. Soc.
Proceedings of the National Academy of Sciences (U.S.)	Proc. Nat. Acad. Sci. (U.S.)
Proceedings of the Physical Society (London)	Proc. Phys. Soc. (London)
Proceedings of the Royal Society (London)	Proc. Roy. Soc. (London)
Proceedings of the Society for Experimental Biology and Medicine	Proc. Soc. Exptl. Biol. Med.
Proceedings of the Society for Experimental Stress Analysis	Proc. Soc. Exptl. Stress Anal.
Progress of Theoretical Physics (Kyoto)	Prog. Theoret. Phys. (Kyoto)
Quarterly of Applied Mathematics	Quart. Appl. Math.
Quarterly Journal of Mechanics and Applied Mathematics	Quart. J. Mech. and Appl. Math.
Quarterly Journal of the Royal Meteorological Society	Quart. J. Roy. Meteorol. Soc.
Quarterly Reviews (London)	Quart. Rev. (London)
Radiation Research	Radiation Res.
Radiology	Radiology
Radiotekhnika	Radiotekhnika
Radiotekhnika i Elektronika	Radiotekh. i Elektron.

15-30

Raketentechnik und Raumfartforschung	Raketentech. u. Raumfartforsch.
RCA Review	RCA Rev.
Reactor Science and Technology	Reactor Sci. Technol.
Recherche aéronautique	Recherche aéronaut.
Recueil des travaux chimiques des Pays-Bas	Rec. trav. chim.
Referativnyĭ Zhurnal Fizika	Referat. Zhur. Fiz.
Referativnyĭ Zhurnal Khimiya	Referat. Zhur. Khim.
Referativnyĭ Zhurnal Mekhanika	Referat. Zhur. Mekh.
Research (London)	Research
Review of Scientific Instruments	Rev. Sci. Instr.
Reviews of Modern Physics	Revs. Modern Phys.
Revue d'acoustique	Rev. acoust.
Revue de mathématiques spéciales	Rev. math. spéc.
Review of Metal Literature, American Society for Metals	Rev. Met. Lit., ASM
Revue de métallurgie	Rev. mét.
Revue d'optique	Rev. optique
Research Trends, Cornell Aeronautical Laboratory	Research Trends, Cornell Aeronaut. Lab.
Rheology Abstracts	Rheol. Abstr.
Ricerca scientifica, La	Ricerca sci.
S. A. E. Journal	SAE J.
Science	Science
Science Abstracts	Sci. Abst.
Scientia (Milan)	Scientia (Milan)
Scientific Papers of the Bureau of Standards	Sci. Papers Bur. Standards
Scientific Proceedings of the Royal Dublin Society	Sci. Proc. Roy. Dublin Soc.
Scripta Mathematica	Scripta Math.
Semiconductor Electronics	Semicond. Electron.
Siemens-Zeitschrift	Siemens-Z.

Sitzungsberichte der deutschen Akademie der Wissenschaften, auf Berlin	Sitz. ber. deut. Akad. Wiss. Berlin
Skrifter utgitt av Det Norske Videnskaps-Akademi i Oslo. I. Matematisk-Naturvidenskapelig Klasse	Skrifter Norske Videnskaps-Akad. Oslo. I. Mat.-Natur. Kl.
Society for Industrial and Applied Mathematics Journal	SIAM J.
Soviet Astronomy	Soviet Astron.
Soviet Physics "Doklady" (Eng. tr.)	Soviet Phys. Doklady
Soviet Physics JETP (Eng. tr.)	Soviet Phys. JETP
Space/Aeronautics	Space/Aeronaut.
Spaceflight	Spaceflight
Space Technology	Space Technol.
Spectrochimica Acta	Spectrochim. Acta
Steel	Steel
Technical Publications of the American Institute of Mining and Metallurgical Engineers	Tech. Pub. Am. Inst. Mining Met. Engrs. (colloq.: Tech. Pub. AIME)
Technical Translations	Tech. Transl.
Technisches Zentralblatt-Abt. Elektrotechnik	Technisches Zentr.-Abt. Elektrotech.
Technology Review	Technol. Rev.
Teknisk Ukeblad	Tek. Uke.
Tele-Tech	Tele-Tech
Tellus	Tellus
Tohoku Mathematical Journal	Tohoku Math. J.
Transactions of the American Electrochemical Society	Trans. Am. Electrochem. Soc.
Transactions of the American Geophysical Union	Trans. Am. Geophys. Union
Transactions of the American Illuminating Engineering Society	Trans. Am. Illum. Eng. Soc.
Transactions of the American Institute of Electrical Engineers	Trans. Am. Inst. Elec. Engrs. (colloq.: Trans. AIEE)
Transactions of the American Institute of Mining and Metallurgical Engineers	Trans. Am. Inst. Mining Met. Engrs. (colloq.: Trans. AIME)

Transactions of the American Philosophical Society	Trans. Am. Phil. Soc.
Transactions of the American Society of Mechanical Engineers	Trans. Am. Soc. Mech. Engrs. (colloq.: Trans. ASME)
Transactions of the American Society for Metals	Trans. Am. Soc. Met.
Transactions of British Ceramic Society	Trans. Brit. Ceram. Soc.
Transactions of the Faraday Society	Trans. Faraday Soc.
Transactions of the Illuminating Engineering Society (New York)	Trans. Illum. Eng. Soc. (N. Y.) (or Trans. IES)
Transactions of the Institute of Radio Engineers (Give appropriate group identification.)	Trans. Inst. Radio Engrs. (colloq.: Trans. IRE)
Transactions of the Institution of Chemical Engineers (London)	Trans. Inst. Chem. Engrs. (London)
Transactions of the Royal Society of Canada	Trans. Roy. Soc. Can.
Transactions of the Royal Society (London)	Trans. Roy. Soc. (London)
Union Géodésique et Géophysic International (London)	Union Géodés. et Géophys. Int. (London)
U.S. Atomic Energy Commission Nuclear Science Abstracts	U.S. Atomic Energy Comm. (or AEC) Nuclear Sci. Abst.
Vacuum	Vacuum
Verhandlungsberichte der deutschen Kolloid-Gesellschaft	Verhandlungsber. deut. Kolloid-Ges.
Welding Engineer	Welding Engr.
Welding Journal, The New York	Welding J. (N.Y.)
Weltraumfahrt	Weltraumfahrt
Wiener Berichte	Wien. Ber.
Wireless Engineer and Experimental Wireless	Wireless Engr.
Wireless World	Wireless World
Zeitschrift für analytische Chemie	Z. anal. Chem.
Zeitschrift für angewandte Chemie	Z. angew. Chem.
Zeitschrift für angewandte Mathematik und Physik	Z. angew. Math. u. Phys.
Zeitschrift für angewandte Mathematik und Mechanik	Z. angew. Math. u. Mech.
Zeitschrift für angewandte Physik	Z. angew. Phys.

Zeitschrift für anorganische und allgemeine Chemie	Z. anorg. u. allgem. Chem.
Zeitschrift für Astrophysik	Z. Astrophys.
Zeitschrift für Elektrochemie	Z. Elektrochem.
Zeitschrift für Feinmechanik	Z. Feinmech.
Zeitschrift für Fluwissenschaften	Z. Fluwiss.
Zeitschrift für Kristallographie, Kristallgeometrie, Kristallphysik, Kristallchemie	Z. Krist.
Zeitschrift für Instrumentenkunde	Z. Instrumentenk.
Zeitschrift für Naturforschung	Z. Naturforsch.
Zeitschrift für Physik	Z. Physik
Zeitschrift für physikalische Chemie	Z. physik. Chem.
Zeitschrift für wissenschaftliche Photographie, Photophysik und Photochemie	Z. wiss. Phot.
Zentralblatt für Mathematik	Zentr. Math.
Zhurnal Analiticheskoĭ Khimii (tr.: Journal of Analytical Chemistry)	Zhur. Anal. Khim.
Zhurnal Eksperimental'noĭ i Teoreticheskoĭ Fiziki (tr.: Journal of Experimental and Theoretical Physics)	Zhur. Eksp. i Teoret. Fiz.
Zhurnal Fizicheskoĭ Khimii (tr.: Journal of Physical Chemistry)	Zhur. Fiz. Khim.
Zhurnal Obscheĭ Khimii (tr.: Journal of General Chemistry)	Zhur. Obschei Khim.
Zhurnal Prikladnoĭ Khimii (tr.: Journal of Applied Chemistry)	Zhur. Priklad. Khim.
Zhurnal Teknicheskoĭ Fiziki (tr.: Journal of Physical Technology)	Zhur. Tekh. Fiz.

APPENDIXES

Appendix A
SAMPLE PAGES

This appendix contains samples of the following:

- Contents page
- List of illustrations
- List of tables
- Page of text
- List of references

Samples of illustrations and tables are included in the pertinent chapters.

For convenience, company document numbers and page numbers have been omitted from the sample pages.

Sample Contents Page No. 1
(With Subheadings)

CONTENTS

[Pagination may be consecutive throughout the publication, rather than consecutive by section.]

Sample Contents Page No. 2
(Without Subheadings)

CONTENTS

[Pagination may also be consecutive by section.]

ILLUSTRATIONS

Sample List of Tables

TABLES

Section 1
MECHANICALLY ERECTED ANTENNAS

1.1 STEERABLE PARABOLA

1.1.1 Introduction

The feasibility of a steerable parabola was discussed in the seventh quarterly report. The present report contains: (1) a design for a "rose petal" parabola, and (2) a discussion of the tracking angles and the angular rates of a steerable parabola mounted on a stabilized satellite.

1.1.2 Beam Steering

Methods. The three available methods for beam steering, listed in order of current usefulness, are as follows:

- Mechanical rotation of the antennas or feeds
- Switching between antennas pointed at various angles
- Phase control

Mechanical steering of large reflectors or linear arrays appears to be the most feasible on stabilized satellites because of the low angular acceleration required. Continuous steering allows the use of a narrow beam, but the converse is not necessarily true. However, a relatively narrow beam may suffice if the steering, although not continuous, is accomplished by judiciously chosen movements.

Choice of steering axes. One possible method for steering is the azimuth-elevation system, illustrated in Fig. 1-1 (Ref. 1). Figure 1-2 illustrates the coverage from an antenna with a fixed angle ϕ as the satellite passes to the side of a ground station. (See also Table 1-1.)

Sample List of References

Section 4

REFERENCES

1. J. J. Hamilton, Reflex Klystrons, New York, Macmillan, 1959

2. J. B. Cladis and A. J. Dessler, "X-Rays From Van Allen Belt Electrons," J. Geophys. Res., Vol. 66, Feb 1961, pp. 343−350

3. C. F. Kooi, W. R. Holmquist, and J. T. Doherty, "Surface Spin Pinning in Permalloy by an Oxide Layer" (paper to be presented at International Conference on Magnetism and Crystallography, Kyoto, Japan, Sep 1961)

4. C. R. Wylie, Jr., Advanced Engineering Mathematics, 2nd ed., New York, McGraw-Hill, 1960

5. S. D. Gvozdover, Theory of Microwave Valves, tr. from Russian by Walter P. A. Hass, R. C. Glass, ed., New York, Pergamon, 1961

6. Lockheed Aircraft Corporation, California Division, High-Energy Rate Metal Forming: Final Technical Engineering Report, 18 Oct 1957 to 1 Aug 1960, by F. C. Pipher et al., Burbank, Calif., Oct 1960 (U)

[References may be numbered consecutively by chapter or section (1-1, 1-2, 2-1, etc.) rather than consecutively throughout the report.]

Appendix B
ANNOTATED BIBLIOGRAPHY

B.1 Books on English Usage and Technical Writing

Ball, John and Cecil B. Williams, Report Writing, New York, Ronald, 1955, 407 pp.

Uses a functional approach, with useful sections on starting a report. Good for the beginning student. Skimps graphic arts, but gives interesting examples and problems.

Barzun, Jacques and Henry F. Graff, The Modern Researcher, New York, Harcourt, Brace, 1957, 386 pp.

An erudite and entertaining book for anyone engaged in research and report writing. Is concerned not only with the historian's approach to sources but with the effective presentation of findings. Includes a useful bibliography of historical writing, composition, and bibliographical aids.

Blickle, Margaret D. and Kenneth W. Houp, Reports for Science and Industry, New York, Henry Holt, 1958, 320 pp.

A workmanlike, straightforward text for practitioners, students, and teachers of technical writing. Reviews the major requirements, divisions, and forms of·publications, including letters, progress reports, and proposals.

Evans, Bergen and Cornelia Evans, A Dictionary of Contemporary American Usage, New York, Random House, 1957, 567 pp.

A lively, readable guide to current English, covering both British and American usage but always from the American viewpoint. Discusses such questions as grammar, word preferences, effective style, punctuation, idioms, and spelling.

Flesch, Rudolf, The Art of Readable Writing, New York, Harper, 1949, 237 pp.

A fundamental book on what makes writing readable. Based on assumptions that have been challenged. Provides a reading-ease score, a rough measure of readability. Must be used with care, for it can lead to baser English.

-----, How To Make Sense, New York, Harper, 1954, 202 pp.

A breezy, chatty book concerned with the art of communication. Contains sound psychological comments as well as debatable disparaging evaluations of such items as grammar and vocabulary building. Includes a new readability formula.

-----, How To Write, Speak, and Think More Effectively, New York, Harper, 1960, 362 pp.

Essentially a compilation from Flesch's previous books and articles. With characteristic oversimplification, stresses the interrelationship of writing, speaking, and thinking. Provides a quick self-test formula and exercises on readability.

Fowler, H. W., A Dictionary of Modern English Usage, London, Oxford Univ. Press, 1926, 742 pp.

Wildly radical when first published, but now considered conservative. A primary authority on difficult and fine points of usage.

Gowers, Sir Ernest, Plain Words: Their ABC, New York, Alfred A. Knopf, 1955, 295 pp.

A literate and sprightly analysis of the crimes of officialese. Contains much material of value to a writer. Good on choice and handling of words.

Gunning, Robert, The Technique of Clear Writing, New York, McGraw-Hill, 1952, 289 pp.

Gives ten principles for clear writing, with readability measured by the Fog Index. Makes assumptions that have been challenged.

Harwell, George C., Technical Communication, New York, Macmillan, 1960, 332 pp.

A knowledgeable book, reflecting tendency of publications on technical writing to stress the rhetorical principles applicable to all kinds of good writing. Includes adequate illustrative material, together with a manual of general composition.

Hicks, Tyler G., Successful Technical Writing, New York, McGraw-Hill, 1959, 294 pp.

A practical "how to" book treating technical articles, papers, reports, instruction and training manuals, and books. Overstresses the commercial aspects of technical writing. Also tends to give pat formulas which presumably ensure "success."

Howell, A. C., A Handbook of English in Engineering Usage, 2nd ed., New York, Wiley, 1957, 433 pp.

A text concerned with the fundamentals of English composition for the engineer-writer. Subordinates discussion of reports to such items as paragraphing, mechanics, punctuation, and grammar.

Jespersen, Otto, Essentials of English Grammar, New York, Henry Holt, 1933, 387 pp.

A precise and detailed condensation of Jespersen's four-volume work. Not a text but a useful desk reference for the experienced writer or editor.

Jones, W. Paul, Writing Scientific Papers and Reports, 3rd ed., Dubuque, Iowa, Wm. C. Brown, 1954, 224 pp.

A systematic textbook for the elementary student. Describes scientific method and analysis; stresses logical construction and development of the report. Includes good additional readings and analysis of different types of writing.

Kerekes, Frank and Robley Winfrey, Report Preparation, Including Correspondence and Technical Writing, 2nd ed., Ames, Iowa, Iowa State College Press, 1951, 448 pp.

Good on tabular treatment and illustration methods, but questionable in its bibliographic treatment. Gives considerable attention to typographic problems and to correspondence. Includes many examples.

Manchester, Frederick A., College English Essentials: A Handbook for Students, New York, Appleton-Century-Crofts, 1954, 427 pp.

An excellent basic text that considers both grammatical structure and style.

Marder, Daniel, The Craft of Technical Writing, New York, Macmillan, 1960, 400 pp.

Stresses knowledge and application of rhetorical principles to basic technical writing situations. Ably explains and illustrates a variety of publications.

Nelson, J. Raleigh, Writing the Technical Report, 3rd ed., New York, McGraw-Hill, 1952, 356 pp.

An old standby, comprehensive and with a broad scheme of arrangement. Somewhat advanced for the beginner, but provides useful background on the theory of report writing. Good on structure and style; contains examples and case histories.

Perrin, Porter G., Writer's Guide and Index to English, rev. ed., Chicago, Scott, Foresman, 1950, 833 pp.

Probably the most useful of desk manuals; one of the few books that can be used for home study. Contains a compact, well-illustrated review of fundamentals (Writer's Guide), and gives answers to many common problems of language and usage (Index).

Sherman, Theodore A., Modern Technical Writing, New York, Prentice-Hall, 1955, 424 pp.

Well organized for broad coverage without great depth. Contains extensive treatment of correspondence and surveys many kinds of technical writing, particularly the informal report.

Sigband, Norman B., Effective Report Writing: For Business, Industry, and Government, New York, Harper, 1960, 688 pp.

A valuable, practical guide for writers in such specialized areas as accounting, management, and marketing. Provides a comprehensive bibliography of bibliographies in the major fields of commerce and engineering.

Souther, James W., Technical Report Writing, New York, Wiley, 1957, 70 pp.

A concise, helpful book, particularly for the engineering-oriented writer. Concentrates on the "design approach" to technical writing and hence on such aspects as analysis, investigation, designing, and application. Inadequate in its consideration of mechanics and illustrations.

Strunk, William, Jr., The Elements of Style, With Revisions, an Introduction, and a New Chapter on Writing by E. B. White, New York, Macmillan, 1959, 71 pp.

A vigorous, uncompromising, scintillating little book on the fundamental rules of English usage and the principles of composition most commonly violated. An excellent guide for anyone who wishes to improve his writing.

Sypherd, W. O., Alvin M. Fountain, and V. E. Gibbens, Manual of Technical Writing, 3rd ed., Chicago, Scott, Foresman, 1957, 560 pp.

Excellent section on the characteristics of technical writing and reader-oriented writing. Emphasizes correspondence, papers, company publications, speech preparation and delivery, and articles. Includes a short, useful reference manual. A rework of the syllabus The Engineer's Manual of English.

Thomas, J. D., Composition for Technical Students, rev. ed., New York, Scribner's, 1957, 460 pp.

A comprehensive textbook, designed primarily for students rather than technical writers in industry and government. Treats style, fundamentals and mechanics, modes of discourse, and forms of the whole composition. Also includes exercises and supplementary readings.

Trelease, Sam F., How to Write and Prepare the Scientific Paper, 3rd ed., Baltimore, Williams & Wilkins, 1958, 185 pp.

A basic guide, with many suggestions to lighten the author's load. Gives clear instructions for do-it-yourself preparation of graphs and for photographing laboratory specimens. Also includes mechanics of manuscript preparation and indexing. Valuable for those operating on a small budget.

Tuttle, Robert E. and C. A. Brown, Writing Useful Reports: Principles and Applications, New York, Appleton-Century-Crofts, 1956, 635 pp.

Presents a comprehensive discussion of the fundamental principles and techniques of report writing.

Ulman, Joseph N., Jr., and Jay R. Gould, Technical Reporting, rev. ed., New York, Henry Holt, 1959, 382 pp.

A basic text in technical writing, practical in approach and attractive in format. Includes material on oral reports, technical papers and articles, laboratory reports, and instructional writing. Contains many examples.

Weil, Benjamin H., The Technical Report, New York, Reinhold, 1954, 485 pp.

> A compilation of papers by many authors. Discusses in detail the government report; also security, distribution, and retrieval of technical information.

Wicker, C. V. and W. P. Albrecht, The American Technical Writer: A Handbook of Objective Writing, New York, American Book Company, 1960, 415 pp.

> A useful text for a course in objective writing, which is "simply good expository writing with practical interest." Divides material into three parts: principles of technical writing, forms of technical writing, and handbook of style and mechanics.

B.2 Style Manuals and Specialized Publications

American Institute of Physics, Style Manual, 2nd ed., New York, 1959, 42 pp.

> Guide for preparation of articles for journals published by the American Institute of Physics. Includes a good section on presentation of mathematics.

Clarke, Emerson, A Guide to Technical Literature Production, River Forest, Ill., TW Publishers, 1961, 182 pp. (plus supplement)

> Subtitled "A concise handbook of production methods," describes such elements of production as organization, operation, and management of technical literature production groups, and the problems of recruiting, evaluating, and training the technical writer. Valuable for the supervisor and those concerned with scheduling and cost estimating.

Committee on Form and Style of the Conference of Biological Editors, Style Manual for Biological Journals, Washington, American Institute of Biological Sciences, 1960, 92 pp. (published for the Conference of Biological Editors)

> Designed for research workers preparing manuscripts for publication in biological journals and for authors of technical reports. Broadly interprets style to mean forms of expression in scholarly writing.

Doss, M. P., ed., <u>Information Processing Equipment</u>, New York, Reinhold, 1955, 270 pp.

A useful reference on kinds of equipment for preparing and reproducing copy. Identifies manufacturers and trade names. Provides extensive bibliographies for individual chapters.

Hall, Ray Ovid, <u>Handbook of Tabular Presentation</u>, New York, Ronald, 1943, 142 pp.

A testy, opinionated work. Gives a penetrating and thorough analysis of the problems encountered in handling tabular material.

Hurt, Peyton, <u>Bibliography and Footnotes, A Style Manual for University and College Students</u>, Berkeley, Calif., Univ. of California Press, 1949, 167 pp.

A valuable guide for handling unusual citations: government and foreign official publications, court decisions, laws, and Congressional proceedings. Weak in technical references.

International Paper Company, <u>Pocket Pal</u>, 6th ed., New York, International Paper, 1960, 126 pp.

A source of useful information on graphic arts, advertising, and printing. Presents a concise discussion of coldtype composition, offset duplicating, photoengraving, offset lithography, and a glossary of graphic arts terms.

Lasky, Joseph, <u>Proofreading and Copy-Preparation</u>, New York, Mentor Press, 1954, 656 pp.

An encyclopedic work dealing with every phase of copy and proof handling. Useful for a publication supervisor who must train his own proofreaders and copy editors.

McCrum, Blanche Pritchard and Helen Dudenbostel Jones, <u>Bibliographical Procedures and Style, A Manual for Bibliographers in the Library of Congress</u>, Washington, Library of Congress, 1954, 127 pp.

An aid to authors in planning and organizing a large bibliography or literature search.

Melcher, Daniel and Nancy Larrick, <u>Printing and Promotion Handbook</u>, 2nd ed., New York, McGraw-Hill, 1956, 438 pp.

A ready reference for typography, illustration, and printing processes, materials, and terms. Handy for the novice in publication work.

Nicholson, Margaret, <u>A Manual of Copyright Practice for Writers, Publishers, and Agents</u>, 2nd ed., New York, Oxford Univ. Press, 1956, 273 pp.

A comprehensive, conservative reference for solving day-to-day problems of copyright practice.

Shaw, Ralph R., <u>Literary Property in the United States</u>, Washington, Scarecrow Press, 1950, 277 pp.

An uninhibited view of copyright practice, considered by some to be too free-and-easy. Suggests much wider latitude in the use of technical material than does Nicholson.

Skillin, Marjorie E., Robert M. Gay, and others, <u>Words Into Type</u>, New York, Appleton-Century-Crofts, 1948, 585 pp.

A useful manual of printing practice, less detailed than Lasky or Melcher and Larrick, but wider in scope.

Spear, Mary Eleanor, Charting Statistics, New York, McGraw-Hill, 1952, 253 pp.

An excellent guide for author, draftsman, and technical editor on the preparation of different types of charts. Emphasizes the relationship between statistical data and graphic presentation, and indicates how purpose as well as audience determines the particular form of presentation. Combines succinct discussions with ample illustrations.

U.S. Government Printing Office, United States Government Printing Office Style Manual, rev. ed., Washington, Jan 1959, 496 pp.

The standard work for GPO and Government administrative agencies.

University of Chicago Press, A Manual of Style, 11th ed., Chicago, 1949, 522 pp.

The most widely used manual for trade and technical book publishers. Has had great influence in standardizing publishing practices. Includes an excellent exhibit of type fonts and foreign typefaces.

Worthing, Archie G. and Joseph Geffner, Treatment of Experimental Data, New York, Wiley, 1943, 342 pp.

Thorough treatment of methods for reducing experimental data to publishable form. Has good material on experimental design and on mathematical analyses.

B.3 Dictionaries and Directories

Air University, The United States Air Force Dictionary, Maxwell AFB, Ala., Air University Press, 1956, 578 pp.

American Aviation Publications, Aviation Jargon, Washington, 1956, 34 pp.

American Institute of Physics, American Institute of Physics Handbook, New York, McGraw-Hill, 1957, 1524 pp.

The Condensed Chemical Dictionary, 5th ed., New York, Reinhold, 1956, 1201 pp.

Gale Research Company, Acronyms Dictionary: A Guide to Alphabetic Designations, Contractions and Initialisms, 1st ed., Detroit, 1960, 211 pp.

Henderson, John G. and Jack M. Bates, Metallurgical Dictionary, New York, Reinhold, 1953, 396 pp.

International Dictionary of Physics and Electronics, Princeton, N. J., Van Nostrand, 1956, 1004 pp.

James, Glenn and Robert C. James, eds., Mathematics Dictionary, Princeton, N. J., Van Nostrand, 1949, 432 pp.

National Aeronautics and Space Administration, Aeronautical Dictionary, by Frank Davis Adams, Washington, U.S. Government Printing Office, 1959, 199 pp.

Standard and Poor's Corporation, Poor's Register of Directors and Executives, New York, 1928 – (published annually)

Thomas Publishing Company, Thomas' Register of American Manufacturers, 1905 – (published annually)

Appendix C

EDITORIAL AND PROOFREADING MARKS

The editorial and proofreading marks commonly used for typewritten material are listed below. Each mark should be indicated not only within the copy but also in the margin. (Unless the number of marks warrants the use of both margins, the marks are normally placed in the right-hand margin.) Placement in the margin will (1) increase the likelihood that the typist does not overlook the need for instructions, and (2) enable the author and editor, in their final proofreading, to verify that all indicated corrections have been made. When a line contains more than one error, the notations in the margin are arranged to read from left to right and are separated from each other by a slash mark (solidus).

Mark Used in Margin	Explanation	Example of Mark Used Within Copy
ϑ or ϑ or ϑ	Delete	shock shock tubes
ϑ	Delete and close up	not useable
⌒	Close up	missile borne
⌒ # ⌒	Close up to one space	reports ∧ were prepared
cap (s)	Capitalize	doppler effect
lc	Place in lowercase	a Pitot tube
cap + lc	Capitalize first letter; lowercase the remainder	MISSILES AND SPACE DIVISION

Mark Used in Margin	Explanation	Example of Mark Used Within Copy
∧,	Insert comma	atomic, molecular∧and nuclear
∨'	Insert apostrophe or single quote	in the low 50∧s
∨" / ∨"	Insert quotation marks	chapter entitled∧Special Facilities∧
⊙	Insert period	12-in∧radius
;/	Insert semicolon	coordinates∧however, two types were
:/	Insert colon	the following theory∧ When several
-/	Insert hyphen	high∧altitude conditions
=/	Leave hyphen in	inspector will spot= check the equipment
1/em	Insert dash	two programs∧Polaris and
(/)	Insert parentheses	transitions∧i.e., line spectra∧
?/	Insert question mark	entitled "Will Nuclear Tests Continue∧"
#	Leave space	molecular∧energy
tr	Transpose letters or words	proposed/program/study/
(sp)	Spell out	Wright-Patterson (AFB)

Mark Used in Margin	Explanation	Example of Mark Used Within Copy
stet	Restore word crossed out; literally, let it stand	~~continuous~~ absorption coefficients
⊗	Replace imperfect letter	feasibility study
insert, see copy	Insert omitted material*	is consistent ‸ previously presented
¶	Make new paragraph	low-pressure tubes. ¶ Other factors
no ¶	Run into same paragraph	the past year. This program consists of
]	Move to right	10.6 0.8]
[	Move to left	10.62 [0.8
⌐⌐	Move up	temperature ⌐range⌐ of
⌣	Move down	temperature range of
⟳	Move to position indicated	absence of patterns (of some types)
‖ or =	Align	personnel facilities equipment
——/	Underscore	listed under the heading <u>Dimensions</u>

---

*When the omitted material is brief, it may be written in the margin.

INDEX